Courage and
stories and

Combat Stress Veterans

Edited by
Siobhán Campbell

Compiled by
Peter Dobson, Peter Pugh, Christine Sterba, Janice
Lobban, Joseph Ryan

In support of
COMBAT
STRESS
They fight our wars. We fight their battles.

Kingston University Press

Kingston University Press Ltd.,
Kingston University,
Penrhyn Road,
Kingston upon Thames,
Surrey KT 1 2EE.

British Library Cataloguing in Publication Data available.

ISBN 978-1-899999-55-2

Set in Garamond
Typeset by PK Editorial: www.pkeditorial.co.uk

Printed in the UK by Lightning Source

Cover designed by Gudrun Jobst: www.yotedesign.com
Cover photograph by Jamie Rowland (see Acknowledgements and Biographical notes)

Courage and Strength

stories and poems

Contents

Foreword

This is a book which speaks to us of uncommon courage and of enormous mental strength. These Veteran writers address their chosen topics with the kind of clear-eyed compassion and insight that comes from facing severe adversity in a way which makes us discover and value our shared humanity.

In these pages is writing which does not shirk from recognising the sometimes life-changing consequences of combat experience. It is also work which can teach any reader about the values of comradeship, courage and a capacity for sacrifice which, at our best, unite us all.

The quality of the writing - the sights, sounds, imagery and dialogue -remain with the reader long after the book is closed. I was transported back to the distinct smell of the battlefield and felt again that particular atmosphere. I enjoyed the humorous approach of some of the writers – soldierly language in its earthy reality - and was moved by the empathy to comrades described by others. Above all, the writing is striking in its range and scope, with a capacity to describe both personal and more public moments memorably and sometimes harrowingly.

The contributors to this volume have shown the qualities of 'Courage and Strength' throughout their military careers and never more so than in facing up to the lasting effects of their experiences. The work of Combat Stress with Veterans has been essential since Service men returned from the Great War. It is exciting that creative writing, like these pages, can be added as one Veteran says, as 'another tool to the therapeutic toolbox', and is testament both to the vision that Combat Stress has and to the work they continue to do with Veterans in their care from all the Services and Merchant Navy.

I am proud to introduce the work of these Veteran writers. We owe a great debt of gratitude to all who serve, to their families, and to those who have paid the ultimate sacrifice. The voices of those who have returned can be heard in their human complexity, courage and strength in this book of stories and poems. I urge you to honour them by listening to those voices.

General the Lord Dannatt, GCB CBE MC DL
Chief of the General Staff (2006–2009)

Acknowledgements

Combat Stress is the UK's leading military charity specialising in the care of Veterans' mental health. Founded in 1919, the charity's aim is to ensure that Veterans receive the right mental health care, in the right place, at the right time. Combat Stress provides specialist trauma-focused treatment at three short-stay treatment centres, as well as practical and clinical support in the community and a 24-hour Helpline (0800 138 1619).

Our work saves lives and is as vital today as it has ever been. Right now, Combat Stress is supporting more than 5,000 UK Veterans with mental health problems, including 284 Veterans who have served in Afghanistan and 637 who served in Iraq.

Grateful acknowledgement to Dr. David Rogers, Kingston Writing School, Kingston University London and the support of Kingston University for the pilot writing workshops held at Combat Stress, Leatherhead.

Sincere thanks for their hard work to the compilation committee led by veteran writers Peter Pugh and Peter Dobson whose commitment devised and supported this project.

Very special acknowledgement is due to General the Lord Richard Dannatt, GCB CBE MC DL for his insightful foreword to the work and to author and commentator Sandi Toksvig for her pertinent introduction.

Acknowledgement to Fire Step Publishing is due for permission to reproduce Liam O'Brien's poem 'The War in my Head' and 'The Great Leveller' by BlackDog661 which both appeared in *Enduring Freedom: An Afghan Anthology* (2011).

Special thanks for use of the cover photo image: entitled 'Pot of Gold' created by veteran photographer Jamie Rowland. This image was created using a photographic technique called High Dynamic Range (HDR) and comprises five identical photographs taken in quick succession, but at equally varying exposures. The individual images are then aligned and stacked on top of each other to create a single image. The final image is then edited to create the finished image. For further information on photographic services:

www.manicmancphotography.co.uk
info@manicmancphotography.co.uk

Finally, thanks to Kingston University Press and to Stuart Bird for his work on this text as well as to Judith Watts, Senior Lecturer in Publishing Studies, for her prowess in production.

Combat Stress is the trading name of the Ex-Services Mental Welfare Society, a Registered Charity: England & Wales No. 206002; Scotland No. SC038828.

Introduction

For someone who thinks of themselves as a pacifist I have written a lot about war lately. Perhaps it is not surprising. We are all subjected to images of conflict every day which come home to us through the television. As the conflicts in Iraq and Afghanistan wind down, the truth is there will always be another place, another arena where men and women behind desks think it suitable to send a younger generation to fight.

I have been working on a novel about a young Victorian woman who, in 1899, decides to escape the confines of the drawing room by disguising herself as a man and going to serve in the second Anglo–Boer War. As I studied the conflict I realised that the war was not about morals or freedom but about money and influence and it made me think about how little has changed.

The Honourable Artillery Company in London provided many Boer War volunteers and my research there led to me being invited to a regimental dinner. As I sat chatting with soldiers serving today, my thinking turned from whole regiments in battle to individuals. Meanwhile my partner, a psychotherapist, was dealing with a number of returned veterans in a private mental health facility. She was enraged by their treatment and came home each day in a state of distress.

I began to read about the effects of war on the individual and of every war's legacy among combatants of all nations – divorce, marital problems, tranquilizer use, alcoholism, joblessness, heart disease, high blood pressure, ulcers and of course, tragically, suicide.

I thought about the young men I had met who had been sent to do an incomprehensibly difficult job by their nation and who, in many instances had not been cared for properly when they returned home, broken inside.

I wrote a play called '*Bully Boy*' which focused on two men's experience of war. I wanted the subject of how we deal with psychological pain inflicted by conflict to be something people talked about. I did my best but all I could think about was how many stories remain untold.

I hope our past leaders read this book and feel some shame. I hope every politician who has it in his or her power to crank up yet another war reads it. I want them to think, for example, about Laurence Hewings who, aged just 19, supervised the body bagging of dead Argentinian young men in the Falklands: to listen to Richard Kidgell whose experiences left him with a sensation of 'barbed wire dragging through my brain'.

This is a world I cannot know for myself. I will never know the horror that so many soldiers re-live through flashbacks but I can have some understanding when Keith Burton tells me:

Flashbacks. Flashbacks? What are they?
Just memories that don't decay.

This volume is full of astonishing work. It is painfully and often brilliantly written and in the midst I found something wonderful about the human spirit. In Lee Harrison's poem *From a Veteran to a Veteran* I found a life sustaining PS when he wrote "There is always HOPE"

This book has hope in it. Thank you for supporting Combat Stress.

Sandi Toksvig

Note from the editor

The role of war writing in all its forms has always been able to engage our cultural discourse. This collection of prose and poetry provides an important continuation of that legacy. Here are stories from many different arenas: the Falklands, Northern Ireland, the Mediterranean, Africa and the home front. Many pieces expertly recount moments of reflection in the field and others deal honestly with ongoing challenges but what links them all is the awareness that a richly textured inner life is the place from which good writing can emerge.

Where a poem that deals with the tsunami is clearly also about the trauma of combat, where lines with great feeling for the natural world are written with acute observational skills, when an empathy towards 'victims' extends to the enemy and beyond, then we know we are in the presence of writers who have something essential to say.

Having been privileged to work with some of these authors in a workshop situation, I have seen the care with which they revise to find the right word, the most apt phrase and the best ending to their piece. Their skills are particularly in evidence when they combine the most poignant detail with an irreverent wit which only serves to emphasise the honest reality of the content.

There is work here which will leave a reader breathless, work which lingers long in the mind and not just because it unflinchingly renders individual experience into literary form, but also because it forces a reader to join in the conversation and to ask the most difficult of questions.

As an editor dealing with these deeply intelligent and humane texts, my job has been to recognise the devices that writers employ to convey psychological truth. The variety of forms and approaches is as expertly handled as the use of surprising poetic turns while unexpected rhyme and sprung rhythm refers us back to the real import of the content. Again and again we are taught by this work to read more closely, to become more aware of how the composition of words can speak to our inner mind, the place these writers reach with this strikingly political and utterly memorable work.

Siobhán Campbell
Kingston Writing School
Kingston University London

THE RIDDLER

The Ball

I kicked a ball, not just any ball,
for that ball meant a lot to me.
It was a simple offer of peace and friendship
from a soldier in the Lower Falls
to Belfast boys aged five and three.

But that ball that I kicked,
it changed the rules of engagement,
and it cost me dear, 'fraternizing with the enemy'.
A severe dressing down
and a loss of pay, times three.

How dare those safe behind desks and in high places
tell those on the ground, what to do, what to see.
That ball that I kicked was an offer of friendship
from an eighteen-year-old soldier,
to two Belfast boys, aged five and three.

A Modern War

Bruce and Ginger, only boys, knew not this modern war.
Alert with weapons outside Woolies on a Saturday
wasn't what real soldiers joined the army for.
Not for us a front to fight on,
a patriotic charge where soldiers knew the score.
Instead an evil enemy around and amongst us,
in this very modern, modern war.

A border patrol, a vcp, a narrow lane with hedges high.
It could even be home, down in dear old Cornwall,
not some evil sinister place to die.
Bruce was my oppo; whom I became a man with,
he didn't deserve war's sacrifice.

Today I am sad, now so many years later,
nothing has changed, history is repeated
with yet another bloody, modern war.

RICHARD KIDGELL
A Light in the Darkness

A road, hard and rocky,
Winding through the Stygian darkness.
Black as pitch,
Never ending night.

Forever it goes on,
Stretching to the end of time.
Forever it reaches backward,
Till the World is without form and void.

And the burden, it is heavy.
It weighs me down,
Crushes me to the cold, hard rocks,
Crawling, sometimes, because the weight
Is too heavy to be borne.

And in the darkness,
Beyond my reach,
I hear the cries...
Gaia weeping for her babies,
The murdered children of the World.

The stupidity, the waste.
The cruelty of mankind.
I must keep going, must keep moving,
For somewhere on that road ahead,
Though wreathed in horror and darkness,
Lies an answer.

But I am blind in the darkness,
And my burden weighs me down.
And the road is harsh and rocky,
And I just cannot go on.

Then a quiet voice speaks in my ear,
And a lantern glows through the dark,
Let me help you for a while,
I will lift your pack, I will light your way,
I will give you respite while I may

My name is Tyrwhitt, the stranger said,
I am here to help the lost souls in dread.
To find their road, to ease the tread
Of those too weary to forge ahead

And he raised his lamp above my head,
And lit the rocky road ahead,
Come, lean on me,
Take strength from me.
The road is easier now, he said.

So we walked together, and talked together,
And he looked at me and smiled,
And I breathed new life and hope inside,
And strength… just for a while.

But, all too soon, the stranger said
He must leave me to go alone
For many souls are lost in dread,
With few like him to guide them home.

But ease your fear, he smiled at me,
I'll not abandon you,
And when you need me most again,
You'll find that I'm there too.

So I took back my heavy pack –
It no longer weighed like lead,
And though the path was harsh and dark,
I had remembered where it led.

Thank you, Tyrwhitt, I shook his hand.
You have given hope in this dreadful land,
And you have, too, renewed my strength
To keep on walking for another length.

And you are right, in what you say,
There are many still weary, as far away
From their path
As I was till this hope-filled day.

He turned away, his lantern high,
A beacon of hope in the starless sky.
Tyrwhitt! I called, and he looked around,
God bless you Tyrwhitt! For today I had found
The strength that would take me closer to Home.

(This poem is dedicated to Combat Stress – The Ex-Services
Mental Welfare Society, and especially to the dedicated staff
of the Tyrwhitt House treatment centre.)

Inside

Deep, deep down inside me,
A black pit.
Ink-black; jet; as dark as night.

With fathomless horrors,
Unknown and unknowable,
Lurking in the dark
All around.

A scream.
Silent, deep, unheard
Except by me.
It is mine –
And I don't even know why.

A pit, black and dangerous,
But somehow safe.
The horrors inside are mine.
Old enemies, but old friends too.
I know them, and they know me.

A quiet pall,
A blanket or a warm shroud.
Terrible but familiar,
Soft and Warm.

Outside is harsh.
Noise sharp and penetrating;
Bright lights that sear the soul;
Clamour that allows no rest.
Never left alone.

Pain – the World is pain.
Inside the pain can be ignored,
It doesn't hurt.
Outside it clamours and demands –
Harsh, like the noises.

The Pit is bad.
Dark and horrible.
Gentle light, pastel colours,
Soothing sounds and solitude
Is what I want.
But that is not the choice.

All I am given is the Pit or Outside.
Nameless silent horrors in the Pit,
Or harsh, demanding, uncaring
Knives in the brain –
Cutting and slashing.
Outside.

I don't know – perhaps that's the problem.
Hero or mouse – which am I?
I like the mouse.
Quiet anonymous. Leave it to others.
Enjoy life for yourself.
Nothing to live up to;
Mediocre;
Nothing to be.

But the hero won't stay quiet.
He keeps coming out;
Excels, takes control, saves.
Embarrassing.

I'm glad he saves, but it's embarrassing.
Why do other people have to know?

A while just to be me.
Quiet in the world of peace and quiet love.
A river; trees; insects and birds.
A gentle hum, a quiet babble.
Warm with spring.
Inside.

But now that's long ago.
Now just Outside or the Pit.
I long to be inside again.
Home.

The Immortal

I was born from a splash of Medusa's blood;
A gout of white steam boiled from the sea by Hera's curse.
My mother's head severed by Perseus, the murderer.
Do you wonder at my hatred for the race of men?

Born in heat, my blood runs cold as ice.
My coat is brightest white, my heart as dark as night.
I was born full grown from the raging foam;
My lungs breathed deep, my wings stretched out,
And I leaped to the sky from the wounded sea.

Lightning hooves flash with thunder.
No man shall ride upon my back,
No god of men shall ever tame me.
I hate all men, but to the equine race I am a God!
I am Pegasus, the immortal.

Three People

To dance the dance of life, the Woman said,
Is what I want to do.
Joyous, loving, never lonely.
But who am I?

Saintly, angelic, dressed all in white,
Kind, loving, generous and respectful.
And yet I am alone;
No partner in the Dance of Life.
They dance on Earth,
But I find it lonely in Heaven.
No one can see me with brightness all around.

I am also dressed all in black,
Sucking in the light, making it disappear
Into the anguished depth of my soul.
I am the World all that matters.
I am deprived the World must feed me.
But I *am* the World, so I am alone.
It is lonely in Hell.
No one can see me in the dark.

I am *in* the World, complex and coloured;
Varied hues, and varied shades.
My life is gayety and strife,
It is generous give, and selfish take,
But there are people in my world.
I dance, I love, and I am loved.

One woman, three people.
Light cannot exist without the dark;

Darkness is lost without light to cast the shadows.
Give and take, joy and sorrow.
These make the Dance of Life.

*(inspired by the painting 'The Dance of
Life', by Edvard Munch)*

Writers Block

Noises, Noises, harsh and jangling.
I cannot think!
People, people inside my head,
Tearing and ripping at my brain.
I am among them,
But I am not of them!

I try to think, but noise surrounds me.
Not loud really,
But it is a barbed wire dragging through my brain.
And I cannot think.
Cannot create.
Struck dumb.
Inside my head.

Please shut up!

The Mask I Wear

Who am I? Do you know me? Perhaps quite a lot?
You think that you do; but I think not.
You see my face so you think and stare.
But the truth is this: You see the mask I wear.

We all wear masks; of course we do,
For others to see us as we like them to.
Courageous, funny, and clever too:
Impress the ladies, our friends as well; helps the career too.

I used to wear a mask like that;
It wasn't false, or at all a lie,
Just a bit of gilding to help me fly –
To soar to the top of life? Great peak.
Too green, too young, to know what to seek.

But I changed my mask when I changed my life,
To show me as calm amid fear and strife.
And this mask I showed *to myself* as well
So that I would stay calm when my world was Hell.

And this mask it worked, for others *and* me,
'Good Man!' they say, and I would see
A job well done, my task seen through.
No fear, no slips but my stomach knew!

A hard sick knot, untied and forgot,
Pushed well away and quickly forgot.
But it stayed right there, in the back of my mind,
Locked safe away and hard to find.

I changed my mask when my life changed again;
Professional, calm, efficient and sane.
But the knot was there, in the back of my mind,
Corrosive, poisonous, burning my mind.

I've ignored that knot once, could I do it again?
Panic unfelt, but giving great pain?
I did well in life, my career ran high;
But with old pain inside, it hurt so much to try.

So I forged my new mask from iron and steel,
And set it in place so that I wouldn't feel
The pain and the doubt
That I'd let people down if I was caught out.

Don't look too good; cover your skill;
With a modesty false, in the background stay still.
You can't let them down
If they expect no great skill.

But the person leaks out the person I am.
I try to keep hidden, keep shut like a clam.
But I do the job right, because I must try my best,
So people expect it, and give me no rest.

It's old and corroded, this mask that I made,
And stuck fast in place on a mind hurt and frayed.
Who am I now? I stand inside and stare:
The hurt tortured soul,
or the soul mask that I wear?

WILL MEANS

In Timeless Rivers

In timeless rivers our love flows,
meandering lost in fast currents of confusion.
At times it bubbles to the surface in joy and in a moment
it seems to sink as if gone, like an illusion.
But if we look, like into a mirror, at our children,
family and those close who surround us,
we will see clearly that our love
is always around us.

LEE HARRISON

From a Veteran to a Veteran

Hello old friend, how are you?
I thought I'd write to you.
I have been talking to time and he agrees that it is
time to change.
I have been given a task.
To write your feelings, especially anger, guilt and shame,
as they have been with you too long.
Time knows your journey has been a long and painful one,
time for those feelings to go.
I have faith in you, and I know that you will do it.
Now old friend, the future is in your hands.
From your old soul that's always been in your heart
call up compassion – love and forgiveness.

P.S. There is always HOPE.

PETER DOBSON

The Tree of Strife

Rooted in slag and ancient bones
The Tree of Strife stands on its own.
Straggly branches thin and bent
Canopy bold and sweeping down.

Causing worry and ailments dread,
Infants caused to die in bed.
Children with rickets bent and thin,
Parents bowed down, worn with care.

Green shoots appear and things look brighter
Look closer see blight destroying
Things look better sky looks brighter
The storm is coming air is cloying

Rise above the trouble
Try not to burst the bubble
All your work will be in vain
The Tree of Strife brings back the pain.

ARCHIE WADDELL

Peter Cairns Brown

You have left your life
of pain and sorrow.
No more anger,
no more tomorrow.

You chose a path
which led you to stray,
but with God's blessing
darkness will be day.

Forget we cannot.
Forgive we might.
We wish dear brother,
you are bathed in God's light.

STUART McGLEAVE

Hollybush

Here loneliness never argues, needs not to
be explained, nor longs for shallow
contracts to in vain feel whole again, here
dazzling beauty shadows me,

captivates each faith-hold tightly, bowls
me over daily, nightly, leaves graces,
senses, shining brightly –

Here, refined inducing aura glistens as
emblazoning gusts embrace every
awestruck moment,

thoughtful process, kindness, calmness
and courteous ways.

('Hollybush' refers to Combat Stress Hollybush
House in Ayrshire)

LAURENCE HEWINGS

Unforgotten Journey – Falkland Islands

Goaded by the ferocity of the force ten arctic winds, grim and ominous swells emerged out of the surrounding blackness and rolled menacingly into steep contours of mountainous rage. They would repeatedly and brutally thrust the ship's bow steeply upwards and out of the ocean, shelving us for a split second, like punctuation, before smashing us down, deep inside the wave's low trough.

It was as if Poseidon himself was expressing his rage at being woken by man's frivolous squabbling and each time the ship rolled over, perhaps too far, meal trays would slide off tables crashing onto the floor. While in the ship's toilets, stale urine, inches deep, would lap the floor covering the feet of whoever was in there at the time and the ship's hull would groan so obtrusively, the noise would stifle the unremitting monotone drone of the massive engines.

I was on one of the several ships heading south and mine was called the *Sir Bedivere*. A virtually flat-bottomed roll-on/roll-off beach landing ship stretching one hundred and thirty seven metres long and just twenty wide, it endured admirably the wrath of the South Atlantic that tormented and threw us around with such vehemence that while we slept in our bunks, we were forced to strap our bodies to the framework using rifle slings, to stop from being flung off each time the ship leaned right over.

Due to the nature of our deployment, we were seriously overcrowded with around five hundred fully equipped personnel on board not including the ship's crew. This meant in the already cramped sleeping quarters, dozens of men were forced to sleep in hammocks hung literally wherever space allowed. At one point, the ship's desalination unit, pushed to its limit, malfunctioned and all showering was banned for a week to conserve fresh water, until it was fixed. The stench below became practically intolerable.

Finally, after three weeks, we sailed within striking distance of Argentine fighter bombers. At night a blackout policy around the entire ship was strictly enforced and this made watch-out duty a perilous task, especially at shift changeover when it involved negotiating your way along the outside decks in complete blackness as the ship rolled precariously from side to side, giant waves crashing over your head. When we eventually reached our position on a standing platform forward and to one side of the vessel, outside the bridge, we tied ourselves securely to the railings using thick rope through fear of being swept overboard.

I remember so clearly that first morning during breakfast when the air raid alarm was loudly sounded, echoing throughout the entire ship, followed by one of the ship's officers speaking through the announcement address system. Firstly, in English and then in Chinese for the benefit of the Hong Kong Chinese crew:

'Air raid warning red. Air raid warning red. Exocet attack. Exocet attack. One three zero degrees. Estimated time of impact. Six minutes. Move to the lower decks immediately. I say again. Move to the lower decks immediately.' In the next few days we got used to this and became rather self-proficient at eating our meals promptly rather than risk having them end up on the floor.

When HMS *Sheffield* was blown up beforehand by an Exocet missile killing twenty of her crew, it was revealed that most injuries occurred from flying debris. For this reason, the drill was to make our way quickly to the lower decks below sea level and lay down covering ourselves with anything possible, for example, by pulling mattresses off nearby bunks.

Lying on the floor waiting for impact, we knew that at that precise moment in time, an Exocet carrying a 165kg warhead and cruising just feet above sea level at 300m/s was heading in our direction. Unsure exactly which ship the missile's targeting system had locked onto induced stomach butterflies and dread of an intensity I never imagined possible. This occurred several times each day until we reached the Falkland Islands. When we finally reached the beachhead of San Carlos Bay, where the strikes came almost hourly throughout the daytime – and always aggressively – I began to seriously consider the possibility that I might not be returning home after all.

The day I climbed up and out onto the outer deck and saw the islands for the first time, we were anchored in San Carlos Bay surrounded by a flotilla of other ships belonging to the task force. The sea was still and barely visible, obscured by a thin blanket of pre-dawn mist that hung low just above the water, and the panorama was swathed in unexpected yet wonderful noiselessness – interrupted only twice by a Zippo lighter snapping shut somewhere in the distance. It was bewitchingly scenic as any English estuary at first light and for the next half hour time stood still as I stood gazing into this real-life watercolour.

Without warning, four A-4 Skyhawk jets shrilled over the skyline and descended, swooping low as they came in fast to attack. They came in so low their pilots were clearly visible, and the noise as they thundered overhead was deafening. Anti-aircraft gunfire could be heard as the jets vanished high into the sky as quickly as they had arrived. On the horizon, the silhouette of a Rapier missile system, abruptly awoken, could be seen rotating, watching, searching for a target.

Their pilots would strike at extremely low altitude, following the contours of the land to avoid detection. Fortunately, often they were so low that when they released their bombs they were hitting the targets before the sophisticated mechanisms had time to arm themselves for detonation. During the period we had to wait to disembark, my ship was targeted and damaged three times by 1000 pound bombs that had hit the side, failing to explode.

The ferociousness of the sorties earned the beachhead of San Carlos the name Bomb Alley, and it was here that I probably experienced some of the most harrowing and traumatic moments of my entire life. Since then, I've had the image of a jet dropping a bomb with the words, Bomb Alley, tattooed on my right forearm.

Spending that length of time on an amphibious landing craft, a floating target, under such extreme conditions made me vulnerable, susceptible and maybe a little humble. Sadly, it wasn't long afterwards when our sister ship, the *Sir Galahad*, incurred at least two direct hits when targeted by three A-4 Skyhawks, killing forty-eight of her crew.

I was only nineteen, and for some time afterwards I wished I had been older because I believed that maybe I would have understood more about why I was there, and why all of those young men had died. I don't mean just only our own, the hundreds of young Argentine conscripts, many of whose bodies were found after the surrender where they were left lying around Port Stanley. Later, under my supervision, they were body-bagged by a small working party of Argentine prisoners.

I didn't realise at the time that when I joined my ship halfway, at Ascension Island, for the final four thousand mile voyage south, it would change my life forever. From the experiences that ensued, irreplaceable and lasting memories were born that nourished and embraced the very core of my soul.

ERIC THORNTON

The Greatest Kiss

Take me still through baited breath,
Holding tight and glowing red.
Impassioned thoughts till after dawn,
You be my Queen and I your pawn.

Take me still when we are young,
the touch of you like the lover's song.
Athletic nights and slumbered days,
squinting awake from the sun's glowing rays.

Take me still before the kids wake,
More silent now, too old to fake.
We move together, I hold you tight,
One more lingering kiss to see us through the night.

Take me still now we are old,
I love you as I've never told.
Will you kiss me as the day we met?
Our parting kiss shall be the greatest yet.

Views through a window

This feeling of injustice that rings in my head
that comes from knowing I should be alive not dead.
This unearthly gaze that I give you all –
does it turn your guts that you never heeded my call
or does it make you feel sick and can you sleep
and live with the secret that you must keep?
Or do you hate yourself for my demise –
look in the mirror and see all you despise.
If that's the case and that's how you feel
then think of me when you eat your next meal.
With your meat and two veg and your glass of wine
think of the scraps from which I had to dine.
Now I see your face and I feel your guilt
As you realise you're part of the world that had my life's
  blood spilt.

Morning Coffee

Devils take me, angels hate me.
People stare, poison pen affair
Mock the afflicted but your mother's addicted.
Gentleman opens doors, turns the corner to pick up whores.
Loving couples arm in arm paying money to the baby farm.
Internet access for all. Watch as governments fall.
Child found after quake taken without permission for
    science sake.
Rushing for your latest date, detectives your wife's
    evidence collate.
Shaking hands at the garden gate as separate people
    attend, relate.
Take one more puff of your fag turn the pages of the daily rag
Monday morning, paper read; chaos turmoil in my head.

Breaking Point

Head bursting with thoughts of life
guilt and my own hate cutting like a knife.
To live or to end it all; what to do?
Either way, the decision I will surely rue.
Forever walking this night through the rain
trying not to think if only I could kill this pain.
Stopping now, where the hell am I who the hell cares?
Strangers rushing past filling my head with hatred stares.
It's quiet now I jump the fence at the side of the track.
Sitting down, I wait for the train, drops of rain fall down
    my back.
Two at once, here I go, on my feet, am I too late to stop?
A coward again, walking back home fit to drop.
Straight to bed, lie to the folks,
use my brain to work out an elaborate hoax.
Talking crap and deceit in my head,
I would do anything now wake up dead.
Pull it together one last time, crawl to the doc.
Can't remember much, see another Doctor, hear more talk.
Waking up, ward 18 in the Royal,
I hope all these doctors can take my head off the boil.

A Real Man

You sit on your arse and watch the world go by,
watching TV you fart burp and sigh.
Argue with the wife and slap the kids,
no-one dares swap the channel, heaven forbid.
Then it's down the pub to spend your dole,
chat up the barmaid with your patter so droll.
You show her your beer gut and tell her when young
how much you'd have spent, how much you'd have paid
to get her into bed and to get her laid.
Then it's back home to the wife and into bed,
you'll hear nothing of lies about her sore head.
So you slap her about and have your fun,
tell her say nothing about what you've done.
Well you know she won't, she's never before,
when you slap her, kick her call her a whore.
But unknown to you, this night's your last
and unlike her life, your death will be fast.
That knife in her hand is for your throat to slit.
Never again will you use those hands to hit.

JOEY JOE McGUIRE

Tsunami Wave

Tsunami, Tsunami, Tsunami wave
you stole the innocent souls on that day.
Widows and widowers stunned in their grief,
orphans are crying alone on the beach.

You rose from the calm and showed anger instead
and now we are counting and mourning our dead.
Tsunami, Tsunami, harsh cruel sea,
now are shattered amongst the debris.

Receded you mock, once more you are calm
Painfully silent are the tropical palms.
Tsunami, Tsunami, why did you need
so much destruction to fulfil your greed?

The world and its landscapes forever are changed
and so are the hearts left in anguish and pain.
We bury our dead and we all count the loss,
Tsunami though distant in silence you watch.

There aren't enough tears left for every lost child
but our memories will treasure their innocent smiles.
Tsunami you're smiling, you think you have won.
How gently you wallow in the warm evening sun.

Tsunami, Tsunami, Tsunami wave,
we'll not forget your horror displayed.
But life must go on and the living will grieve
and remember the dead that you chose not to leave.

A Late Spring

The daffodils are late this spring
There's not much time to grow.
Just as they lift their golden crowns
It's almost time to go.
The blossomed trees in full display
A glorious sight to see.
The sun shines through the cotton clouds
To bring the spring to me.
The birds are busy nesting soon
The fledglings, they will fly.
I hope to taste the joy of spring
For years before I die.
Drunken snowdrops, moss-dappled roof tops
There for all to see.
I'll linger by forget-me-nots
Near my magnolia tree.

The Cinder Path

Courage forms the heart of a nation and it is found in
  many places.
It comes from those who aspire to better themselves,
those who would go that extra inch
or those who would burst their hearts to achieve an extra mile.

Courage is fought for and is found in the bare grit
  of determination.
It is fuelled by the desire to win,
it is the will to rise up to the challenge and it is found in the
  most unlikely places,
its seeds planted in the young.

Courage is not only found on the battlefield
but elsewhere, in other fields.
It is found in small hearts as well as large
and it makes every corner of our land its home.
It is the very stuff that built our nation.

Courage is the essence of our being.
It is in the 'cinder-track' waste from the hearths our people
crushed, then pounded by the feet of our youth.
It is in the tears and joy that the Olympiad never fails
  to deliver,
every raised trophy is born of courage.

Courage is seen on every pathway and spreads quickly when
  its face is shown
to lift the hearts of those around it.
So they too may find the strength to pound that cinder path
whenever its challenge presents itself.
Yes, that is courage.

RAY HEWITT

The Enemy

There's something that I want to say
About what happened on that day.

When I left you alone back there
Please don't think I did not care.

It's just that I was scared of you
And wasn't sure what I should do.

But if I could get back to that place
I'd close your eyes and kiss your face.

Then dig your grave and say goodbye
To the soldier I watched die.

KEITH BURTON

Abducted

Quick boys, the gun, get the gun
before the helicopter comes,
you're ours now fella, we'll beat you black and blue,
you'll wish it's all over, before this night is through.

We want names and addresses, so just give
this information that we want so you might live.
You were stupid enough to come to our patch
'cause lookouts are always on the watch.

The bowling alley and cinema complex –
it's fools like you this place attracts.
Yer da and uncle and granda too
can go on the list of our killing crew.

Quick boys, get away
the helicopter's on its way.

(On Quick Reaction Force at Portadown with 3 Royal Irish, a part-time soldier was abducted from a local leisure complex. A swift intervention undoubtedly saved his life, but not before critical inform-ation about other family members in the regiment had been extracted.)

Catching Up

Last night I saw my old friend Mac
we sat together chatting at the back
of his country cottage with the pub next door.
He knows the landlord well, that's for sure.
Talked about old times, how our lives progressed,
it's been twenty-nine years since we last shared the zest
of young men's lives full of hope,
the reality of life and learning to cope.

The beauty of that balmy evening
the glorious scent of late spring
helped solemn discussion at our core:
the sacrifices of that Falklands War.
He, injured in that bombing run
terror inflicted, my own mind torn.
But we laughed and joked and had a pint
next door in the pub, late at night.

Alas all too quickly, time to go,
why is it that sometimes time goes slow
when life is hard and nothing is right
and you've lost the very will to fight?
Yet with long departed it goes so quick
and with absent friends, comrades stick.
Time went so quickly or so it seemed.
Time to wake up from my state of dream.

The Bombing of 846 Squadron

A distant booming disturbs my sleep
and I sit up and touch the sides of my self-made tomb

in the darkness my exaggerated sense of touch
reveals the roughness of freshly dug wall

whilst the cloying of sweat and fear
warns me of impending doom

It's ok, it's far away
comes a disembodied voice

of one standing watch in the night
Go back to sleep, tomorrow's a new day

But sleep cannot come now
and I lie awake in the darkness

thinking of my family, far away.

Flashbacks

Flashbacks. Flashbacks? What are they?
just memories that don't decay.

The surge of adrenaline that fear brings
within helpless reach of Death's sting.

Perfect memory, sweated brow
intruding in the here and now.

Tortured, Killed and Dumped

I ease off the tablets at one fifty
'cause they make me dopey and less nifty
but a drawback it seems
is that I remember my dreams
and I feel out of sorts and shifty.

Last night once again I was chased
and caught by those men of low base.
I was shot in the leg
and for mercy I begged
but my face was beaten to paste.

When they had all I knew
and their efforts were through
I had a bullet to the back of the head.
Dumped along the roadway, I woke up today
not sure if I really was dead.

The Colleen

Down to her shoulders a glorious dark mane
and eyes of blue appraising the strain
of rhythm and rhyme narrated by men
trying to find the stillness of zen.

With singing lilt she further expounds
the tensions and qualities that abound
within the poetry of traumatised men
trying to find the stillness of zen.

Gesticulation and smiles with wide-eyed glow
she bids adieu and off she goes, *Salanche va (Slàinte mhath)*
poetic Colleen helping us men
find the stillness of zen.

(Within the stillness of meditation there is found healing and the ability to process traumatic memories. Siobhán Campbell from Kingston University helped pilot the creative writing scheme at Combat Stress and has certainly helped this client devise another tool for the therapeutic toolbox.)

The Wolf

Gentle tapping side by side
uncovering passions that deeply lie
within the subterranean depths
of unconscious thinking – I wept

I saw the wolf within his lair
waiting for death from the air
his savage, relentless snarling,
straining at leash, jaws bearing

vicious teeth with total lack
of compassion for those in merciless attack.
Come back, come back, the Therapist says,
she brings me back to here, today.

(My first crack at EMDR (Eye Movement Desensitisation and Reprocessing) led me to identifying the Wolf – the killing savagery that arises during a fight or flight response. The Therapist's intervention is vital to enable successful processing of the traumatic memories.)

Sunset

The freshening stillness settles down
on uniformed men gathered round,
the marching band in proud display
the evening hymn at the end of day.

Converted top deck to helicopter pad,
a musical call o'er the sea, so sad,
red-tinged eye sinking low –
universal witness as southbound we go.

But who could see that purple hue?
In ominous thoughts each man withdrew,
across the heaving endless sea,
forever gone – will it be me?

Internal chatter in surreal silence,
throbbing funnel enhancing poignance,
fate draws us on this brooding trip –
the liner *Canberra*, war-bound troopship!

Red and Green harmonious sound,
ceremonial beat as the sun goes down:
Paratroopers and Royal Marines
sailing to combat the Argentines.

The orb extinguished, greyness, still,
to the South Atlantic at Parliament's will.
Within each man darkness falls,
duty-bound Sunset ceremony calls.

(I joined a writing group and 'Sunset' was set as a theme for the next meeting. For several days I struggled with the memories of the Falklands War because 'Sunset' triggered the above memories into the chain reaction. Writing the poem helped to settle me down again.)

Jersey Battle of Britain Remembrance

A church by the park, warm September sun
hails the heroes on holiday, as to remember they come
the sacrifice of another generation
mostly gone but never to be forgotten.
Courage to turn back the tide
of National Socialism that had flooded Europe
and the sanitized version of war is remembered.
But I met a Spitfire pilot once
Battle of Britain, shot down, baled out
and his mind damaged by the stress
of mortal combat in the air.
Stories of drinking and banter
down the pub to contain the fear
an aircraft wobbling in the air
and slurred speech through a tinny transceiver,
ampoules of morphine settling raw nerves.
Such behind the scenes stories
do not hold well with a believing public
who hold their protectors on high
but these stories are regularly told
along the labyrinthine corridors of Combat Stress,
where the brokenness is resolved.

(Holidays for Heroes Jersey hosted our holiday in September 2010, during the 70th anniversary of the Battle of Britain. Attending a Memorial Service with our hosts I remembered meeting a Spitfire pilot during one of my earlier visits to Combat Stress.)

Landing Craft under Fire

(Extract from journal, 29/08/10)

A difficult start to the day thinking about an ongoing family situation. The anger has brought out the Wolf – a label for the killing rage that can come upon me during periods of dissociation that was identified during one of the many memory therapy sessions at Combat Stress – and I want to tear someone's eyes out. I try to clean the toilet bowl but my mind is full of rage and aircraft are deafening my hearing. This has led to a spaced out head, headache and the Landing craft attack. Somehow or other I manage to get it on the computer …

We loaded onto an LCVP (Landing Craft Vehicle Personnel) about 3pm from the *Canberra*. Skies are blue and weather and visibility is good with flat sea – no problems loading with our heavy bergans.

Beautiful scenery-is this real and was this morning? Experiences real? Was lunch real??? Continual air attacks have come on since this morning bringing a sense of surrealism.

Chugging away like a leisure cruise we are soon reminded of the reality of the situation we are in – this is a war zone and it is quite a way for the LCVP to take us from anchorage to the pier at San Carlos Settlement (5 miles?)

Air Alert Red-Attack Imminent!

The landing craft is expertly brought alongside one of the anchored ships – why? I don't know – after this morning's experiences all I feel is fear. This is not an exercise. This is for real, and myself and Pony Moore on our GPMG (General Purpose Machine Gun) along with Mac and Eddie Edwards on their GPMG have inflicted death on one Argentine Pilot-I realise now that I am writing this from the perspective of Aug 2010 with all the other accumulated crap of the past 28 years which is influencing my stress response in this present moment!

Nothing happens-someone remarks that the incoming aircraft

have been shot down – good effort Navy Harriers!

This happens several times during our tour of what is to become known as Bomb Alley. I have in my mind 3 occasions. The final Air Alert Red whilst afloat brings us alongside one of the LSLs (Landing Ship Logistic), the great high grey wall of the ship's hull dwarfing the landing craft (am I remembering this detail so clearly now because the previous incidents on the water passed without danger?)

The GPMG is firmly held into my shoulder with the gas parts (immediately below the barrel) pushed and secured against the chest high rail of the landing craft. My arc of fire is eastward facing down Bomb Alley and we are close to shore (400 yards) on my right (south) and the other north shore about 1 mile to my left. The sky is clear and I feel determined to do my job whatever that may entail with everything I have and that is expected of me as a Royal Marine.

Anticipation without fear.

Roaring of aircraft filling the air with fear and confusion – where is it? I see nothing in front of me – the sky is clear. I make ready (prepare the weapon for firing) but have I been given the order? Gus Pearson RSM (Regimental Sergeant Major 40 Cdo RM) is behind me 'Steady, Paddy, Steady,' he says reassuringly over the increasing roar of the aircraft.

I shot with Gus on the Corps shooting team at Bisley last year and he was also my CSM (Company Sergeant Major) at RM Poole – there is a bond of trust beyond the normal rank structure and I will respond to whatever he expects of me (is this where I now need others around me to guide me today?)

The roar drowns out everything – no target – the fear flushes within me – Steady. The Bofors on the topdeck above and behind us are constantly going boom boom boom but still I cannot see the target-it still doesn't dawn on me that the aircraft is approaching from behind me-I just have a ferocious need to expend my fear and determination on the enemy but still the sky is clear and I am confused-where is it? 'Steady.'

A shadow passes overhead-deadly slow and there is no longer any noise. I notice the distinct Delta wing of the Mirage-I've never been this close to a combat aircraft before.

The shadow of death banks immediately to the right and I swing my gun around, finger on the trigger ready to unleash my own destructive force. But the angle is acute and the gun begins to slide to the right on the rail where it was previously secured-we are at the bow of the LCVP facing out over the starboard edge-other guys are at the stern of the boat and if this gun falls to the deck it may accidently go off and we may have some casualties brought on by my own hand!

The sound is back on again and I see the afterburner of the Mirage flare as the aircraft continues to bank and climb out of the killing zone. All of a sudden it is all over and as I make the weapon safe I can hear giggles and laughter at the stern of the boat – nervous laughter of men who have been conditioned to develop a sense of black humour despite the circumstances – even risk of death!

When death does come amongst us then we laugh no longer at it-we begin to realise the true meaning of remembrance is forced on us the hard way and that we have been spared and given life where our friends have paid the full cost of combat.

This is no longer a game – the stakes are high and the losses devastating!

What do I feel now?

The anger and rage has subsided and the Wolf is settled. Feeling pretty exhausted and headache more settled-still feeling spaced out and things a bit unreal. Did this all really happen to me?

What am I going to do about it?

Writing this has eased off the extremity of the dissociation but I need to just lie quietly to get myself settled again-I am totally exhausted.

JANET DOWNS

Invisible Wounds

Wandering down the dark tunnel,
Headlights hit me, hit the wall.
I see a shadow –
a shadow of my former self.
Somehow it isn't right.

I see a shadow of my former self,
confident, gun-cocked,
trigger finger tense,
a soldier among soldiers, but,
somehow, it wasn't right.

Because I am a shadow of my former self,
I hide in the shadows of my home,
but here, in the dark, there's a connection,
the shadow and I, boot to boot,
knowing it isn't right.

In my painting, the shadows,
battle-black, face each other,
joined by a visible band, boot to boot,
blood red tramlines,
and still, it isn't right.

(This poem was inspired by a Culture Show Special (BBC2, 11th October 2011) which examined the role of art therapy in the rehabilitation of ex-service personnel suffering from post-traumatic stress disorder. One picture was sketched by Smudge at an art therapy session organised by Combat Stress. His final painting now hangs in the Ministry of Defence.)

PAUL LOMAX

Why

I went not knowing, came back fully understanding.
Apprehension became anxiety.
Willingness became why?

Guilt became second nature.
Hurting becomes natural.
Crying eases pain,
numbness eats the mind.

Where is the man that went off to war?

For he has returned empty, unkempt, uncaring.
He is
still in the desert.

England's Youth

As you pass me in the street
it's not the timing of your feet,
I see from your stance you don't feel threatened
perhaps my past would well be beckoned.

For once an enemy right there stood,
his face was covered, like yours with a hood,
but words he did not unleash at me
it was belt fed, or RPG.

Aware again I stand and stare
looking for cover, not here not there.
This is my country, I am at home,
you stand and stare, you're right I'm alone.

But fancy your chances, and you will see
that killing machine is still inside me.

My Old Desert Boots

I still wear my boots,
The suede outer worn with sand and sun,
The soles worn, fabric stained sides,
The miles they have covered,
The sites they have witnessed,
My boots provided me comfort,
My boots are my own,
My boots are still my contact with my past,
My boots now carry me along different streets,
But wearing them I still feel the comfort,
I still feel the strange sense of security they provide,
Maybe one day when I am gone, you will come across those
    worn old boots,
The soles worn, fabric stained sides,
But they will still be my boots, and hold my memories.

Rock
(Mortar attack, Baghdad, 2004)

My life never flashed before me,
childhood, family were absent
as the explosion subsided, the smoke cleared
no thoughts of good times, happiness.

My head numb, my body throbbing
the smell of cordite hanging in the air.
I try to stand and fall.

My mind tries to comprehend what happened in the last
    few seconds
This woman of total understanding and compassion is my wife.
She is my rock.

Chaos, screaming, figures moving through the haze
again I try to stand, my legs trembling, I run my hands over
    my limbs.
I am whole
in the darkness, I feel a hand gripping mine.

The voice I know so well eases the shock,
Sweetheart, it's okay. It's just a dream.
She is my rock, she holds me as I wake.

LINDA FOULKES
Night

Kicking and twitching all through the night
Kicking and twitching through fear and fright
Dreaming and dreaming where nothing is right
All I can do is hold him tight.

Arms and legs flinging to and fro
Fighting off some terrible foe
Dreaming and dreaming where nothing is right
All I can do is hold him tight.

Terror and horror plague his mind
Stuck in a landscape where nothing is kind
Dreaming and dreaming where nothing is right
All I can do is hold him tight.

Shouting out loud and screaming hate
Whispering softly, *It's okay. You're safe*
Dreaming and dreaming where nothing is right
All I can do is hold him tight.

MARK WALMSLEY

A Resurrection of the Eleventh Hour

There was not one single way to say
when enlightenment came my way.
This not the time to count up the cost
of possessions and dreams from a life that's lost.
From a life confined under key and lock,
being sent away, banished from my flock.
Turns not it was not dereliction of duty
That led to the loss of a life's precious chattels and beauty.
Sorry Di, you were my best friend, my wife
destined to share our troubles and strife.

Would that I could and could have turned back the clock –
no dirty laundry aired in the legal eagles judging dock.
My lords and ladies will define what was yours and mine
standing astride some divisive demarcation line.
Oh dear reader, do not be depressed
by my sentiments expressed, memories regressed.
So much was lost, but yet more is gained
as old powers and skills are regained, retrained.
From the depths of a dark deep psychosis
came the hope of a reasoned diagnosis.

Precious time for a little reflection on a hopeful new direction.
Wise owls at Tyrwhitt to woo a disbeliever –
why not become a high achiever?
Refreshed reborn renewed,
fresh hops imbued not brewed.
Hope a substance not chemically created
to a smile newly liberated.
Maybe to others I can give

new direction a place to live.
Negate the negative, oh what fun to be positive
friends and family that's relative.

OT *not* ET

OT the land of occupational therapy –
cast off your care, end your worry, give thanks to the good
   people of Surrey.
There was a race with no face, no number
who people perceived as dumb or dumber
perhaps begging the price of a cup of tea
whose personal plight was of no interest to thee and me.
Polished diamonds, discarded gems
existing in a word of us and thems.
A candle in the wind that had burned so brightly.
Discarded, forgotten, afraid of the light.
To your amazement a dull lustre of what was burnished gold.
One story sadly seldom told
became uplifting a joy to behold
for those that are ignorant of those lives
who took the duckings executed the dives.

RICHARD BORYER

Sweet Summer Smell

The smell of sweet summer
The warm sun
The birds' song
Oh how blessed it is

Then the other smell of summer
comes in the air
the smell of barbecues
that burning smell

I am no longer here
I am back, back there
In the sands of the desert
with all those oil fires

Oh how long for those smells to go away

CHRIS MOORE

The South Atlantic 1982

Beyond your face so vast and deep
where so many brave servicemen lay asleep,
where breakers come rolling in
you treat a mother's tears as no more than a whim.

Your vast exterior tells no lies –
the evidence apparent in a lone mother's eyes.
Your bleakness and greyness say it all,
what was the meaning of this short but bitter war?

Thirty years on we still try to comprehend
ask why the tears seem to never end.
Unshackle us from your icy depths,
let our lives go forward with meaning and breadth.

RICHARD PEACOCKE

Double Tap

It's hard enough, at this remove,
to call up names and faces lost.
But, then, I find they don't approve
of all that *sandbag talk*

of Falklands War; of cold N.I.;
of long-dead friends; of comrades gone;
of girlfriends known; of sex passed by;
of matching knife to gun.

They don't believe – those men in grey –
how hard we had to strain and fight.
I don't suppose their lives contain
even one horrendous sight.

How could we know in innocence
that when we marched and trained and ran,
we would be asked to cross the fence
to kill our brother man.

They tell me – those that wield the quill –
that I had joined for Queen and land,
and then they hid behind me, safe,
as guns jumped in my hand.

My bullets flew, so straight and fast,
to take a soul to its rest.
To leave me stood alone at last;
alone within my breast.

No-one shares the act with you;
no-one helps you squeeze one off.
It's your choice; it rests with you,
to make that weapon cough.

For ever more, in night and day,
in fields or on city's street,
whether you're at work or play,
his eyes yours ever meet.

You'll see a shadow, hear his step;
believe he sleeps nights with your wife.
You'll feel again the double tap;
you'll take again his life.

Nor ever will your sleep be true,
not rest nor peace live in your soul,
until he has forgiven you,
and you are once more whole.

SHAUN A. JOHNSON

Summertime Days

There is something about the summertime days
engulfing the cold in its magical ways.
This brings people out of the long wintry spell,
to a world that's embraced in a flowery smell.

Near nakedness beckons as people dress down,
converting pale skin to a deep golden brown.
Dark sunglasses hide those wandering eyes
that stare at the fair sex in shape, form and size.

Music is welcomed where nothing's too loud,
as it drifts slowly by like a velvety cloud.
Chatter, laughter, smiles broad and wide,
everyone seems to be on the same side.

The evening is quite long yet it's calm all around,
reducing the light seems to settle the sound.
There's a moment when dark steals the brightness away
but in six hours' time starts a new summer's day.

ANGUS BINNIE

Assault

World War II's D-Day assault received much publicity and rightly so – but another important sea-borne assault took place later which did not quite get the same degree of publicity.

This happened on November 1ˢᵗ, 1944 and involved Canadian troops, Commandos, British and European, and me of the 52ⁿᵈ Scottish Division. The latter were trained Mountain Troops, destined earlier for an attack on Norway, but that idea having been dropped, they were now on their first action in Holland, below sea level!

The assault on Walchern Island in the Scheldt Estuary was essential to clear shipping access to the Port of Antwerp for the build-up of supplies before the thrust into Germany's heartland.

The island was heavily defended by established and well-trained German soldiers who understood the strategic significance of the Allied need to command Walchern. Casualties in attacking forces were likely to be high as landings were due to take place all round the island and in the event, the troops, once ashore, were hampered by flooding as the dykes that had held back the sea were breached, courtesy of the RAF. The previous evening (incidentally Halloween), a spectacular, noisy bombardment by massed Allied artillery had relentlessly shelled the island's defensive positions.

I was an eighteen-year-old King's Own Scottish Borderer (4ᵗʰ Batt) and a member of 15 Platoon, 'C' Coy, chosen to be the leading platoon going onto the beach and into the main town of Flushing. We took off around midnight in a landing craft, packed like herrings in a barrel. We landed, at first light, in knee-deep water and sandy sludge, ready to battle up the beach and face whatever the enemy had in store. The Germans were ready and waiting despite suffering the earlier bombardment. Fortunately, the tide being nearly full, the beach was a short one.

Each man carried, in addition to his normal equipment, a heavy case of mortar bombs which we thankfully dumped in the lee of the beach wall. So far so good. We quickly left the beach to enter the dockland streets, the docks themselves being to our right.

Almost immediately, we suffered our first casualty. A German sniper's bullet hit the ammunition pouch of a man in the leading section. The pouch contained a smoke grenade and the phosphorous in it exploded, setting alight the whole front of his body. He collapsed in a doorway and Dutch civilians – an old man and two women – appeared from nowhere with a blanket to smother the flames. The call went up for stretcher-bearers – a call we were to hear too often in the days and months to follow.

Having to pass by this wounded man was a moment I had long dreaded. As a small boy, I had never been keen on the sight of blood from cut fingers or skinned knees. Badly wounded men, no matter how tough, no matter what army they belong to, scream in agony for their mothers – as if it is an instant regression to infancy. No amount of training prepares you for such an experience. Hearing that cry in the middle of the night can somehow make it even more harrowing.

However, as we pressed on past, I had none of the reactions anticipated. Deepest sorrow, yes (he was the best soldier in the platoon), but that was it. My reckoning since then is that we were all keyed up with adrenalin and so our normal sensibilities were blanketed. One quickly learns to 'shut off' feelings since every front line soldier has to face the fact that his life hangs constantly on a thin thread. We were all to see many more wounded, dead and dying men as time went on. All were horrific, but none seemed as horrific as that, our first ever casualty.

Making headway up the streets became impossible as the Germans had pill-boxes commanding every intersection. So, to reach our objective which was the primary school, we took to the back greens of the houses and made our way over fences, walls, hedges, wash-house roofs and through gardens and tool-sheds. It paid off. The only problem was crossing a road, in full view of a pill-box manned by German machine-gunners. But that will have to be another story!

All in all, it had been a nerve-wracking morning – a morning like no other. And it was just the start ...

PETER PUGH

For my beloved

(The following four poems relate to my precious relationship with my wife. Without her love, I would not be here.)

An Embrace

I embrace you with my heart,
But caution;
Before you enter in,
You must know that
Within the caverns of my soul,
Lurk dark and brooding friends,
Courage then,
Let our hearts entwine,
Then in tacit silence
Or touch of eyes,
You will be certain that
I love you.

For My Distant Love

There are many moments like hours
Here in my peopled solitude,
That are savaged by the realisation
That your gentle presence is denied.
Oh, that I were in a dream
And could wake
To find you with me.

Sweet Dreams, My Love

In these lonely even' times
Twixt Life's deception and
Dream's reality,
My body craves you,
Yet my heart cries,
Be still!
Mere distance cannot rent
Your blessed love,
Be still!
And be united
In your slumber

Immediacy

Claws
Of
Anxiety
Grip tight and rip
The chest within and
Eject
All compassion for
Oneself and
Tighter
Ever
Tighter
So that all is
Black
Beyond recognition
BUT
It is
Dawn
And my
Beloved
Hugs me and whispers
I am here
Leave me not
Just dream
With me

Providence?

Blinding light. So intense. My eyes hurt. I can't see!
Crunch!!!!
Blackness.
Gentle light seeping into my brain.

'Where am I?'

'In bed you idiot!'

Oh my head, and my bladder. Bladder!

'Yes, yes I am getting up … yes now.'

What a night. It was great to see Peter and all the guys again. Must have been the first time we have all made it since Helmand? Days that are ever present; but a blink away. That was months ago.

'Wake up! It is almost three years.'

Yet it was only last night …

'No! I am not going there!' … Not again; not now.

Peter saved my life and therefore he must take responsibility for me. Laughingly he announced to all and sundry,

'… or pass you on you bastard! Come Saturday you'll be in safe hands – well, arms. And you'll get kisses – now that is something I just won't do!'

I am so lucky to have a mate like Peter. We had been there, what? Eight or nine weeks I think. The novelty had worn off and we were into a routine. If you can call sand, flies and chlorinated drinking water routine. Oh we did have the occasional 'excitement' of the erratic inbound round or two. Of course we would respond by chasing off in the direction of the fire but only to find people as scared of us as they were of the firing. As blind to us as they were of the bastards that had been shooting. Who is protecting who?

Our advance had been gradual, but that night we were assigned to a surge. The night was clear but strangely and ominously silent. They knew we were coming and they would attack. But when …

SSSSSSSHHHH …. *CRACK!!* Round upon round incoming. Mostly high and wide. Not very clever and we could see the flashes from their weapons.

Within seconds, well minutes, we were ordered to advance on the right flank. Peter signalled that we were to follow him in a tactical formation. The going was tough as we were in the moon shadow of the ravine, but we were gradually gaining ground on their flank. Slowly, slowly catch a …

BANG! Blinding light … Where was I? Dazzled and on open ground! Diving for the deck I smashed my face into a rock. Dazed I fumbled for my weapon, but before I could do anything all hell let loose. That's it guys let them have it. My turn, if only I could get into position … then thud. It was Peter landing alongside me. God he has guts …

'Just lie still! I'll get you safe!'

And you know he did. How can you thank someone who risks his life for you in such a deliberate calculated way?

But Peter where are you now? You are not in your bed. Crashed out on the sofa then? No!

Ah! I remember: Girl Friend. Well an ex two removed at least. Just how did the gorgeous Jenny know where we were partying? Bachelor booze ups were never his scene. And I know where he is. Cuddled up to that lovely lady somewhere. Bastard! He should be here looking after the Groom. It is his duty, indeed his destiny after Afghanistan.

Well I can see that he has the rings, they are on his bedside table. As for his best man's speech, well, provided he is not hung-over it will no doubt charm all assembled. Like many big guys he has a great sense of humour and charm. He will look after me. No, me and my lovely wife Mary, for indeed she will be my wife.

OK but it does leave me to sort out our luggage and tickets for the honeymoon. I know we should have done it yesterday but the guys turned up in dribs and drabs and we had to welcome them all didn't we? Anyway it is all here apart from Mary's bag and passport.

Mary!

I was supposed to meet her and get her stuff. What time is it? Oh no! I must have slept all morning. Why didn't she phone? Well perhaps she did but my mobile needs charging. I'd better get over there now and leave this to later. That is before I meet up with my parents and brother later tonight. Now I haven't seen him for some time, indeed when he emigrated I was convinced that I would never see him again.

I raced over but they would not let me in, something to do with dresses and bad luck so I was sent round the back. There she is; stunning in the evening sun. Her glorious blond hair radiant against her father's brilliant white lilies.

'Oh, My Love, I am late. I am sorry.'

'Hung-over more like! Anyway it doesn't matter. Mum has been chasing me around all day and Dad is up and down. Losing a daughter gaining a son … to say nothing of the arrangements which he is constantly churning over and over. Anyway come tomorrow it will all be over.'

'Just starting My Dearest! I can't wait …'

'I know, I know but it is their day too. It's not every day that they get a daughter off their hands. Just think of the money he will save!'

And spinning round and curtseying she adds impishly,

'But are you sure you can keep me in the manner to which I am accustomed?'

'You are my life, my soul … my hope. How could I

refuse you? ... Let me give you a hug!'

'Oh no kind Sir! For that is a privilege reserved for my husband, tomorrow. I promise. Meanwhile you may give me a quick peck on the ... cheek!'

I did just that. Skipping away she chirped,

> 'Now here is my handbag – with my passport in it. Now you have to go or you will be late for your parents. Dad said he will put my bags out the front. Now go!'

> 'I love you'

> 'I love you too'

Blinding light ... I am dazzled in the sunlight by a gentle tear or two. There is my future. A time at last when I may live for each day in her loving presence and forget the vicious, vivid memories that haunt me. I linger for an instant to take this sacred moment in. I shall treasure this for all of my life.

> 'Oh Peter, thank you saving me for this glorious, wondrous gift of love and life.'

Then I am off. The traffic is just crazy. Just where are all these people going? Don't they know I am in a hurry? Hope Peter has got back. Well his car isn't here and of course he is not in the flat. In fact it looks as if he hasn't been here at all. I put my phone on to charge and call him. Just get his answer phone,

> 'Peter, Peter where are you? You know I need you here so that I don't mess everything up.'

Well it is down to me then. First let's get Mary's bag from the car and put her passport with the tickets. What did I do with her handbag? What time is it? Oh hell, I am late. Well I think I have everything I will need all laid out. Just need to stuff it in the case. Well actually pack it carefully otherwise it won't fit. And thinking about it, what does all this, and Mary's stuff weigh? Can't leave that 'til tomorrow. What time is it? Oh hell, I am really late!

Well that is done. For better or for worse. Must not complain the car has started ... that would have just rounded everything off. But! Oh hell! Look at the petrol. How could you have been so stupid? Can't go through town because of all those other idiots. I know; I'll go round the bypass. Just take it easy and I can fill up near my parent's hotel later. Trust me.

Bloody hell! Not even half way and you are spluttering. Come on old girl we can do it. But no, she gives a last gasp and we coast up on to the grass verge. Never mind I'll give Dad a call and he can come and rescue me. My brother will love it. Phone? Where is the phone? Plugged in, in the kitchen. Have to thumb it then. Anyway it will give them something to laugh about tomorrow.

Typical! The idiots couldn't go for more than a few yards without stopping in town. Out here they just whizz by without so much as a glance. Perhaps if I stood on the road they will see me. Here comes one all lit up he is bound to see me ...

Blinding light. So intense. My eyes hurt. I can't see!

Crunch!!!!

Blackness ...

EDWARD (TED) OGLE

Betrayal

On wings of dread my thoughts they fly
To times and places long gone by
To times of tension and constant fear
In wars for causes that were never clear.

Our duty bound us to the task
'Twas not our place to ever ask
If what we did was right or wrong
Our job to simply quell the throng.

To the empire's corners we were sent
Never questioning what it meant
For we trusted those who'd sent us there
Believing that they'd treat us fair.

But when we returned our sanity shattered
To the powers that be only money mattered
So they kicked us out and washed their hands
Of those who'd fought in foreign lands.

Betrayed by those whom we had trusted
Our lives, our futures all were busted
Betrayed by the callous mercenary band
Of so-called men who run this land.

Betrayed by leaders whose sole concern
Appears to be how much they earn
No thought nor care for our well-being
Our hopes and dreams all sent reeling

A covenant made with a shilling sealed
They sent us off to the foreign field
To live or die they did not care
It was us not them who were going there

Our Lord's betrayer was well rewarded
Thirty silver pieces he was awarded
But our price for being so willing
A single solitary silver shilling

Soul

Amid the ruins of a man once proud
a tortured soul sobs aloud.
The pain it bears is beyond belief –
no hope, no future, no relief.

Confidence shattered, spirit smashed.
Peace and joy cruelly dashed.
A soul that once held high ideals
and now no longer knows to feel.

The things it's seen and has to bear –
result of decisions by men of affairs,
twisted this soul to something obscene,
from fear and hate of things unseen.

In abject anger, it howls its hate
at the world that reduced it to this state.
And in its tortured search for peace
it prays for death, so the pain will cease.

P.T.S.D.

P.T.S.D. what does it mean –
this terrible thing that is never seen.
What is this thing called P.T.S.D.?
Why is it here to torment me?

P.T.S.D. is blighting my life,
not just mine but also my wife's.
P.T.S.D., this terrible curse,
makes mundane problems frighteningly worse.

P.T.S.D., I hate your name,
forever playing your loathsome game.
P.T.S.D. your name's a curse
making my life forever worse.

P.T.S.D. you made a coward of me.
Afraid to think, afraid to be.
P.T.S.D. you're functioning well
to make my life a living hell.

P.T.S.D. you destroyer of lives
of soldiers, their friends, families and wives.
P.T.S.D. your noxious name
is set to drive me totally insane.

P.T.S.D. I cannot hide.
My thoughts can turn to suicide.
But then P.T.S.D. you would have won
as surely as any terrorist's gun.

P.T.S.D., I can't let this be
I have to fight you, not just for me.
P.T.S.D., you're incredibly strong,
but what you want me to do is wrong.

Every day, I must try my best
Despite your total lack of rest.
I know I have to daily tread with care,
I know you're always lurking there.

Thanks to my friends along the way,
I try and manage every day.
To live my life with hope and pride
and daily fight this beast inside.

The House

When first to Tyrwhitt House I came
my mind was low and full of shame.
Convinced that I was going mad,
a frightened creature weak and sad.

Afraid to speak and show my heart,
I felt alone, a Thing apart,
unaware that others here
also felt this raging fear.

The early visits caused me pain
as awful shame I lived again,
but through my grief and through my tears,
I saw that no-one mocked my fears.

And from the staff so quiet and calm,
came a sense that to us no harm
would they permit or let befall
despite the fact we cursed them all.

Bit by bit and through the years
I learned to realise my fears
could be met and faced with pride,
my shameful past I need not hide.

At Tyrwhitt as my trusting grew,
with friendly faces that I knew
I felt that here there was a place
where I could show my real face.

So now each time I come to stay
as I arrive on that first day,
I feel the warmth and safety there
my burden now again to share.

The treatment starts, it's seldom kind,
as different ways I try to find
of coping with this vicious curse
while praying it will get no worse.

DAVE PAYNE
Camber/ Rye Harbour Poems

Haiku

Low tide, water gone
Autumn sun sinks in the sky
Harbour empty again

Sonnet

The tide has all drained away
leaving nothing but gullies and sand
in this harbour that services the bay.
Now is the time to fashion castles by hand,
the setting sun casts a timeless view –
a late October Sunday with an airy nip,
sand and setting sun holds a golden hue.
This place a haven to many a ship,
no Patrick McGoohan running from huge balloons,
though there has been a Dalek or two seen here
where Cliff and the Shadows acted like buffoons
on these very sands settling right here.
But these sands are a death trap,
lost ships lie below their golden cap.

Free Verse

No more windjammers with tanned sails,
that was another era many years ago.
Then came steam, but now it's diesel,
the shipping is now just a dribble
like the river draining to the sea.

There has always been a haven here
but the river took a different path.
That was until the great storm of 1287.
It diverted the River Rother.
Now it empties out here.

These sands are on reels of celluloid and tape
From *The Longest Day* to *Carry On*
Not forgetting *Summer Holiday* and *The Prisoner*,
and Cinderella Rockefeller sang on their bed.
Some locals were scared of Dr Who's enemies!

But now it's just fishermen and tourists
that pass these golden sands
glimmering in the October sun.
Round the seasons go, tide in and tide out,
on and on until the sands of time run out.

Oh What a Lovely Christmas

HMS *Rye* had been in the Gulf for four months. When the four minesweepers arrived, the summer had just ended. To the ships' crews, it felt like living and working in a blast furnace, constantly being fed by the golden expanse of the desert which soaked up the sun's rays and heat like a giant solar sponge.

The temperature between Iran and Iraq was getting hotter. Saddam Hussein was flexing his muscles by gassing Kurds and bombing Iran. In an effort to stop Iraq's oil-rich prosperity, the Ayatollah Khomeini retaliated by sewing the Gulf with mines, hoping to sink the tankers conveying Iraq's oil.

Rye spent her days performing the thankless, nerve-sapping task of minesweeping. In daylight, she swept the main shipping routes, by night she used her sonar. It didn't matter whether the sea was like polished glass or if there was a storm. The job had to be done.

Today was the last day before Christmas Eve, and the three minesweepers were working off Bahrain. The day had been the usual routine of streaming the sweep wires, then hauling them in again when they had swept their designated area. Then, turn around and begin again! This time they streamed an influence sweep. This involved using a buoyant electric cable that formed a loop when towed behind the ship, and when an electrical current was pulsed through it, it turned into a big electromagnet. They also had to stream a five-foot barrel-shaped object called a T.A.G. This reproduced the sounds a ship would make under water. Both of these devices would then hopefully trigger off any acoustic or magnetic mines.

The day ended with the sun on its slow dive to earth, turning the cobalt blue sky first to orange, then to many shades of red, until it had sunk below the black smudge of the desert lands, leaving the high clouds resembling large balls of pink candy floss.

The sea also changed colour from its aquamarine blue, to a mixture of colours reflected from the sky. The surface was turning from an oily smooth to an angry mass, as a desert storm drove off the land and out across the Gulf.

Within thirty minutes the waves had built into steep walls that slammed against the side of the ship, making her move in awkward jerks. The wind howled through the ship's superstructure; spray rained down with each exploding wave.

Eventually, the Captain gave the order to stop minesweeping, but all the gear had to be hauled back in. After one and a half hours, all that was left in the water was one sweep wire, with its torpedo-shaped float attached. And something called an otter was there too. This kept the sweep wire out on an angle away from the ship. Ten minutes passed and the otter and float were banging and jerking on the stern.

'I need someone to lean out and unshackle the gear' shouted Jumbo Hallesey.

'You gotta be fuckin' jokin' replied Yorkie Cockram.

'You know we can't leave it there, not in this shit' answered Jumbo.

The sweep crew looked about and mumbled about having to do this task.

'Someone's gotta do it!' Jumbo shouted again.

From behind the huge minesweeping winch, a figure lurched towards the crowd.

'Yeah, I'll do it' shouted Dodger.

'Just as long as one of you fuck bags keeps 'old o' me legs. I ain't gonna be washed into the drink, okay?'

Dodger tied a rope round his waist and lay down on the wet deck. Armed with a pair of sidies, he inched over the stern. As the ship pitched and tossed, the stern sank into the sea. One second the water was ten feet away, the next he was part of the boiling wake of the ship as the waves surged up and along the sweep deck.

Eventually he dragged his soaking body back aboard to a round of applause and shouts of 'Well done' from above his head. The remainder of the ship's company, who were not on watch, had gathered on the canopy deck to watch the seamen at work. One voice cut across the rest.

'Able seaman Long, my cabin,' commanded the Captain.

After changing his clothes, Dodger made his way to the Captain's cabin. On entering, he was greeted by the Captain and the First Lieutenant.

'Here, drink this. That was a fine spot of work you did there,' said Lieutenant Commander Stanhope, thrusting a large glass of brandy into Dodger's hand.

'Oh, and take this to share between the rest of the sweep deck hands.'

He presented Dodger with a bottle of Johnny Walker black label. After sharing the whisky with the remainder of the Muppets, Dodger and his friend Dave slipped away to the sweep deck. In the white glare of the canopy deck lighting, they sat upon the Jumbo float and sandy bottomed the remainder of the bottle. Their drinking was constantly being interrupted, by waves flooding the sweep deck as the ship buried her stern into the seething malevolent waters of the Gulf, creating a small metallic island within the confines of the deck itself.

0800 the next morning, HMS *Rye* gently felt her way into Dubai docks. In a fairly neat line, the seamen stood as still as possible as the deck rolled beneath their feet.

'Cor me fuckin' napper don't 'alf 'urt,' exclaimed Buck Buchan.

'Yoos ain't the only one, and me guts is a bit rough,' replied Pisser Hill, as a long whining moan weaved around the men, followed by an enveloping blanket of bad eggs and methane.

'Jesus, wot the fuck did you eat last night?' asked Buck the gunner.

'I didn't fancy wot the turd skinner woz cooking last night, so I made meself an omelette.'

'You're sure them eggs were fresh? Either that or you need pulling through with a Christmas tree, fairy end first!' commented Leading Seaman Andy Prowse.

'Stand by to come alongside' came the command from the ship's Tannoy system.

Half an hour later, the ship was secured alongside the dock.

During the day the ship's company went about the usual harbour routines of cleaning the ship, bringing in stores of food, drink and fuel and dealing with any urgent maintenance. Andy Cameron the radio yeoman found time to secure a small Christmas tree to the top of the mast, as is the custom with British ships at Christmas.

Later that night, the Junior rates were being waited on by the Officers and Senior rates in the traditional Christmas dinner. There was only one main passageway aboard and it was being used as an impromptu dining hall. A long table constructed from empty beer barrels with plastic catering trays for the legs and sheets of plywood borrowed from the fire fighting lockers for the top, ran half way down the Main Drag.

At the after end of the passage, where the funnel casing split in two, stood a forlorn but proud artificial Christmas tree. From the myriad of pipe-work hung some scraggy, balding tinsel and a few torn foil garlands. Gently the tinsel and garlands flashed in the glare from the neon lighting strips as the ventilated air moved by. A small piece of tranquillity in the dangerous and volatile situation that every man faced daily. The only sound to fill the passageway was the clamour, shouts and laughter of forty-five sailors gorging themselves on a full Christmas dinner and copious tins of beer.

After dinner, it was time for Secret Santa. The presents were fashioned from anything the men could 'acquire' from around the ship. Jumbo received a plaster cast pointing hand with an inscription that if his finger wore out, he could use this to pick his nose. Dodger received a couple of Jack cartoon books. Spot McLeod ended up being the proud owner of some dumb bells. When the cursing and name calling had died away, two dark figures skulked along the upper deck and sat below the ship's gun, surrounded by the semi-quiet of the docks. All covered in a mix of moonlight and orange floodlights that ringed the whole dockyard. In the shade of the gun, two small red dots from cigarettes occasionally flared, then dimmed.

'The cook fucked up tonight.'

'Yeah, that wuz bloody nice, trouble is though, I think I need a stick and skateboard to carry me gut.'

Both men agreed by groaning.

'Yah know wot Dave, we could be anywhere in the world.'

'Nah, we couldn't. For one thing Devs, it's December an' it's warm. It ain't like this back 'ome.'

'Yeah, suppose you're right Dave, jus' wishful finkin' really. Still a week's time an' they fly us 'ome.'

'I ain't lookin' forward to tomorrow, sailin' at eight on Christmas fuckin' morning f' Christ's sake.'

From a distant part of a ship, a door opened releasing the sounds of drunken men slurring their way through 'Silent Night', then suddenly cut off as the door thudded shut. Slowly the ship fell silent as men drifted away to their bunks.

By 10am, she was back at sea in the area to be swept. It was a quiet day with nothing much going on except the usual ritual of extracting sea snakes from the sweep wires each time they were hauled in.

Christmas night/Boxing Day morning, the ship was mine-hunting, half of the ship's crew was on watch, manning the guns, sonar sets and other positions about the ship. The action station's alarm shattered the nocturnal activities. Those asleep leapt from their bunks, frantically dressing while running to their required positions. Ten minutes later the ship was ready at action stations.

Manning the 40mm gun on the foredeck, Spot, Dodger, Devs and Buck stood waiting alone in the dark. Again!

'Wot's all the flap about then?' Devs enquired, still yawning.

'We've 'ad a signal come frew saying there's gonna be an attack on an oil platform,' answered Spot.

'Yeh? But we're off Bahrain. Nowhere near Kharg Island or the Iranian coast,' contended Buck.

'That's as may be, but apparently the Iraqis fly over Saudi and Bahrain and then on to their targets, 'Spot informed them.

Without warning, the omnipresent drawl of an American's voice filled the night air.

'Attention, all Iranian oil platforms, this is the USS *Enterprise* broadcasting on Channel 16. You have thirty minutes to evacuate all personnel.'

The information was relayed through *Rye*'s Tannoy system.

'Fuck, some big shits gonna 'it de fan den,' Devs said aloud to the gun crew.

The minutes ticked agonizingly by. No-one spoke. The air was now so thick with tension and apprehension, it seemed as if time was being stretched and those thirty minutes were the longest that anyone aboard the minesweeper had ever known.

'Look wot's that, over there to port?' shouted Dodger.

'All oil platforms, this is the USS *Enterprise*. You have thirty seconds, twenty-nine, twenty-eight, twenty-seven, twenty-six, twenty-five ...' came the bodiless voice counting down the seconds as if time were literally running out.

The gunnery alarms rang shrill, breaking the silence of the oppressive darkness. The metallic sounds of the Tannoy system harmonizing with the gunnery alarms, blurting out its information.

'Target bearing red nine zero. Angle of sight. Two zero.'

From the darker line of the horizon, a black shape rose and headed towards them. In what seemed the blink of an eye, the shape was above them, splitting the night apart. Three times the blacked out jet fighter circled the ship before it disappeared away to the east. The infinity of the night sky absorbed the jet, even the sonic assault from its engines lost their superiority to be heard, being replaced the growl of *Rye*'s own engines, punctuated by the occasional hiss of spray as the ship moved across the black waters of the Gulf.

'It's a fuckin' good job they didn't fire. We wouldn't 'ave stood a chance, not at the speed that mother fucker was goin' at,' remarked Buck.

'Three. Two. One. All units engage targets,' the American voice commanded.

The eastern horizon lit up, as far as was possible to see, with big white and orange flashes, as if someone had organized a giant fireworks display, and we heard the unmistakable boom of heavy artillery exploding. In the glow of distant fires, the blurred shape of an oil platform abeam of them, was now ablaze. All personnel in a position to see the macabre spectacle stood frozen. All over the ship, an unearthly stillness descended.

'Fall out from action stations. Starboard defence watch close up,' the Tannoy screeched, breaking the blanketing silence.

The forward guns crew remained still. Each one watching helplessly, trying to imagine the horrors taking place, as oil from the deep below the Gulf erupted in a fountain of fire. The men had a good idea of what was happening, as they had witnessed the attack of an oil tanker a few weeks earlier. The images of little flecks of flame that ran about the deck, where men had been covered in the thick black gold that had been ignited, would never leave their minds. Not even the copious amounts of alcohol they had all drunk when they got ashore had extinguished the visions.

Slowly they all turned their backs on the giant orange and yellow flares dominating the eastern sky. With low murmurs and whispered conversation, those not required for the defence-watch drifted below to sleep.

From somewhere on deck a lone voice shouted '*Happy Fuckin'
Christmas*. Ha!'

JAY ASHWORTH
Can We Commit To Heart?

Can we commit to heart the loss at the Somme,
As we can practice the remembrance of Armistice Day;
Does Normandy ring the bells of our conscience,
When at the Cenotaph, the poppies we lay.

Lest we forget each crisis, present and past,
Afghanistan, Iraq and the Balkans;
Lives and minds of the carnage and fracas,
Palestine, Ireland, Korea and the Falklands.

The many lost, with no flags for victory,
Who fought and died to protect the homeland;
Those who still live to tell their story,
The silent veteran, who still shudders at a bang.

The modern war, fought with technology and lives,
Lost and won in a foreign land,
A senseless act or is it better to fight,
For peace and harmony, and a life so grand;

For those who live in the writings of a memorial,
Remember them all, including their kin.
For those who fade, their memories a pictorial,
They have succumbed to war; they have seen.

JIM WELSHMAN

Sleepless Nightmare

Birds all singing. It is 4am.
Pillow is hard. I'm yawning again.
Sleep eludes at this time of day.
My head is full, no space inside.
Dreams were bad. *Help me!* I cried.

I crave the light, the new dawning day.
Give me some rest. To God I'll pray.
I know he'll help, won't turn away.
I promise to be good, do all I'm told.
Just a night's sleep … worth more than gold!

ALAN WALKER

My Name is Cochise

My name is Cochise
And I am an Indian Chief.
I hunt the plains for buffalo
Beside the banks of the Ohio.

My camp is big with many a snow
And on occasion we go to war
With Blackfoot tribe that lives next door
There is no blood and no-one dies
Touched with coup sticks, our victory cries.

Then came the men from overseas
That raped and killed my family,
Trampled, squashed and ruined feed
And labelled me a savage. Indeed!

Where are my sacred lands,
Where are my people?
Our tepees gone.
Just church and steeple.

When it comes my time to die
And meet great spirits in the sky
I'll stand before them all and cry
I'm Cochise. Please tell me why.

GRAHAM WOODHALL

Clacton 1959

We heaved the bell tents into position and made them stand erect; they had to be our home for another ten days. Pegs well in, walls sheeted and rolled, the door flaps tied back for the day. The next thing we did was fill in the paillasses with straw which the farmer provided, tying them off at the end. We laid them in a radiating circle from the centre pole, ready for testing; looking very comfortable.

Make your own ablutions, Captain said. What, dig a hole? So we did and put up the screens. 'It were just a plank across a hole' but it was done better than any professional could have.

I'm starving I thought, so we lined up in the marquee. It was red hot in here, the walls well down, much noise of chattering boys. Lunch was served and mine had a caterpillar in the lettuce, it was half-eaten – strange I thought – but it was good grub all the same.

The farmer rolled by on his tractor towing a combine harvester, the grain wagon followed and we were invited to stand in it as the grain shot in from a spout above us. Not only was it grain and seed, but all the animals and insects picked up by the combine – a crawling mass of life in the raw. Lots of boys jumped out at this point and left us as we bounced across the land towards the farm. It was up to our waists and the farmer's wife gave us a helping hand to the ground, pockets full of grain. I remember we all enjoyed that trip!

The evening came and the sun melted into the ground as the chill came in from the sea, last post sounded but I was half asleep by then, cosy and warm below my blanket; breakfast would be soon. Oblivion enveloped me and I slept soundly, not dreaming if I recall. It was misty then as breakfast called, a few feet from the floor. I could see quite far from low down but not as far when I stood. Water splashed cold on my face from the tin bowl placed on the trestle. I didn't have time for soap as all the other heads bunched around and I was bundled on my way.

That summer seemed to go on forever and I don't think any of us wanted to return home. The sun shone unendingly and the world was a great place to be in. Alive would be an understatement. It was a great holiday!

LIAM O'BRIEN

The War in My Head

The war in my head seems unfair
something I live with but cannot share.
Heartache and sadness I cannot cope,
though tablets and therapy are filled with hope.

At night the demons come to light
trying to sleep but still in the fight.
Waking in sweats threaded with fear,
face pale and soaked with tears.

My life will never be the same
flooded with guilt and dreaded shame.
Watching folk live and having their fun,
it hits me hard, am I the only one?

The feeling I get when it comes to a head,
wouldn't it be better if I were just dead?
All I want is a better life
for me, my head and my future wife.

GRAHAM WOODHALL

Eternity

It's here now; around
Our massive world; abound.
On the fence, I rest
Clean air, in my chest
The view to see; and listen
Smell the touch, reflections glisten
The wood is rough; dead
Filled with life, decayed
Natural warm. Soft yet hard
Enclosing; looking over; yard
Hedges green, inline row
Land tilled, near to sow
Contours roll, to the sty
Puddles lay, reflecting eye
Beasts, birds; insects fly
Wind blows; busy sky
Nimbus boils; stormy soon
Moisture forms, hail and gloom
Gold star haloes, around a cloud
Gate crashes; extremely loud
A squall; descending
The noise; things upending
Peace no more, for the time
It will abate, down the line
Calm surrounds, a peaceful mind
The view before; for all time
'Tis peace now, shoulders fall
Worries gone, forget them all
Hammers yellow, dip and weave
Nit of bread but no cheese

Rapid wings; buzzing dragons fly
Hoverflies still; hanging in the sky
Grasses; full of seed
Rattle, with every breeze
It is too nice, a place to spoil
The earth, its life; its soil
Enjoy it now, afore it's gone
There is no time, it must be done
The hell we've wreaked, upon this place
Will not forgive our frantic pace
When we have gone, it will reform
And grow again as if by norm
The balance be, correct again
It will remain; eternally

England

Americans think (or maybe not!)
of us poor souls in England.
We live in rags, where wet engines run,
and nightingales fill the air.
It is them, they have a Queen,
whom they so revere.
Anthems they sing, to praise their king
and glorify all wars.
Yet they know nothing of our history,
or of countries which make up the realm.

'Tis like them all to cast disdain
on others they do not know.
They call us low but need us now
to help them with the strain.
The trouble they cause around the globe –
we'll bail them out again.

When they are here, they like it a lot,
the noises and the weather.
The fog, the bus, the taxi; the hell for leather.
We sting their healthy pocket
but it doesn't matter much.
They have a lot, give a little to the poor.
Let them rot, they deserve no more.

The many celebrations that we have,
with bell and trumpet roar,
no week goes by without some more.
The bands will play and march around
triangle to the fore.

Much noise we make and let them think
that's all we are.

We have our countryside –
buzz, meow and bleats abound.
The buzzards soar, the sparrow's sound
all chirping from a cloud.
The crow may crow from lofty perch
but somehow they still don't know –
they don't see what it is we have,
nor do they want to know.
It's true we love them really and try
to tell them so. We don't mean to diss –

But ignorance is bliss!

Touch

I contacted mother earth to enable me to sand smooth a piece of wood which is also from the earth. I was using a piece of sand paper, made by man. Yet, nature also provides; Arkansas stone which we use for smoothing or sharpening.

Sand paper is thousands of small cutting edges laid out randomly, stuck to a paper backing then dragged over a less solid material with force to remove protrusions from its surface, thus making it much smoother in the process.

Sand paper is warm to the touch, and only feels rough if you move your hand sharply across it. It can cause a burn to the skin while doing this or even remove the skin's surface if rubbed too vigorously.

The small pieces of rock stuck to the paper are as old as the earth itself, made up of a miraculous mixture of differing stones, shell, bones, salt and a myriad of other elements. Yet, we touch it often with no thought as to its past history or where it has come from.

What did it look like a million years ago? Was it a cliff face, a man's skull or part of a diamond? It's not that we don't think about it, it is just there, another use of nature for our benefit.

As with many things, man has copied nature, he has simulated nature's natural abrasives. Dry salt, sand on the skin, wood on the beach, it contrives to make things smooth and pleasant to the touch; our skin does not like rough things, our touch reacts to that feel, it is alien to our new modern softness.

Touch accounts for many things we use; shoes, gloves, eye protection, thimbles and the pumice stone, which we use to remove hard skin from our body.

Touch teaches us about many things.

Touch.

PAUL PERCIVAL

Anxious Monday

I'm feeling really anxious now it's ten past nine at night –
why has it hit me now, today had been all right?
I saw the Doc, P.T.S.D. group, tried to keep on top.
I'm really tired of being ambushed, from where I know not.
It's like having two brains, one functions pretty well,
the other domineering one takes me back to hell,
The lads notice the jumping, anxious, no control –
Please Paul go and lie down mate, before you take a fall.
I ask myself why do I keep on coming here again.
The answer is quite simple, I pray for a miracle to take away
    the pain.
I will fight this awful crap that pops into my head,
digging deep, searching, hoping for someone to explain
why for no apparent reason up pops my domineering brain.
There's no control over anything and anxiety reigns again.
I'm embarrassed of the twitches, jumping and tics,
I hate the fucking bad dreams, medication that makes you sick.
All in all a sorry mess, so I had to write it down
It's like fighting back, taking control, tell myself
    Get a grip, you're Paul
Just remember you're not the only one to very nearly fall
Just get up, that's all we can do, and if we give up fighting
anxiety will win through.
And if I let it win, here lying on my bed,
I'll be just another one P.T.S.D. made dead.

Homeless

As I lay on the floor of this multi-storey,
so cold,
so wet,
sleeping bag soaked, strong alcohol to forget.
I hear a noise, what could it be?
The spirit of the demon has come at last for me.

It has already taken all of my friends,
I'm the only one that's left.
God please help me, it's not my time.
I tell myself drink more booze Paul,
you'll be fine.
Don't be afraid, don't close your eyes.
Then bright lights, and again that noise,
then Oh! That awful truth appears,
that noise, that realisation,
the spirit of the demon

is in me.

RICHARD GILDEA
Whispered Tears

He stole a whispered moment, which caught me by surprise
I turned to let him know, 'twas a way not often shared
In words so soft and gentle that betrayed his hurt filled eyes
Reaching out he touched my heart, the sweetest *Thanks* I've
   ever heard

My view of him from rear was of a man with huddled frame
Propelled by wheels misfortune, marked by service
   to the Crown
His strength of arms emblazoned by the Regimental name
His useless legs no longer bear the world that
   weighs him down

In youthful times oft' dreaming of adventure and renown
   in life
Confronted recognition, sometimes simply much
   too hard to bear
Reflection now screams back at him of troubled times ahead
   with strife
A future once of sun filled days, for love's young dream
   without a care

In hearing of my words, expressing all his hopes and fears
Articulated in a way he'd oft' times prayed so hard to say
Buried deep in memory, suppressed throughout
   the darkened years
Had somehow reached inside his mind, this burden to allay

Heaven's Tears

Precipitation from above, unto the earth doth sate
Pouring forth in torrent daring feathered friends to soar
Perched on wooded bough, their stifled song 'til morrow waits
Blooms potential harmony in lifeblood's thunderous roar

Bumbled buzzing creature, pollen search abated now
Fragility of wing beat, precluding sorties in the air
Hovers to keep busy, 'tis all that he knows how
Honeycombed design etched deep upon a canvas rare

Soiled rivulets hath formed, beneath the shadow of a tree
Puddled pools warped image, reflection of a former self
Smooth washed surface offered face, hides moss filled
     side of lee
Standing caked in weathered bark from frozen winter's shelf

Autumnal breeze caressing brow, before the flowered soil
     turned cold
Abrasive winds that scored, sun kissed countenance of youth
Will spring be the redeemer, sally forth to be so bold?
One lasting long hot summer, afore I go to face the truth

Open Day

Fleet Air Arm 'Open Day at Yeovilton'. We had been given an assignment which required building a 'Footbridge' across a busy dual carriageway. This would provide pedestrian access during the 'Open Day'. We were just coming to the end of our Field Engineering training at Southwood camp, Cove, Farnborough. This was seen as an ideal way of putting our newly acquired skills to the test and at the same time to help our naval friends!

The first thing that struck me on arrival at Yeovilton was the naval terminology. When entering through the main gates, we were indeed actually going 'On Board'. When leaving the camp we were officially going 'On Shore'. The Fleet Air Arm flag was flying on a ship's mast which had been supplanted close to the Guard Room (Brig).

The 'Footbridge' was quite substantial because of the numbers anticipated for the Open Day! 'Bailey Panels' were used for strength and stability, during the build. This was carried out in the hours of darkness on the Friday Night.

It became noticeable that a few of our Senior NCOs began to disappear during the build! It didn't surprise yours truly, as I had already noted the steady stream of beautiful Wrens going 'On Shore'. I put it down to privileges of rank! (I made a mental note to achieve promotion as soon as possible.)

We completed the task in hand with some time to spare and so were able to get some sleep before the 'Big Day'. Our Naval chums were so pleased, that we were allowed to use all of their facilities. The food in the Cookhouse (Galley) was fabulous, and everything was spotless. I was beginning to wonder if I had joined the wrong branch of the services! I then witnessed a Petty Officer carrying out a kit inspection of young Cadets. At that moment I realised that I had made the right choice.

To all of you Army lads out there, especially 'Sappers', our training inspections were like being at 'Billy Butlins' compared to this! Before we left the 'Fleet Air Arm' base, we had to liberate our Troop NCO, who had been thrown in the 'Brig' for fraternising with the Petty Officer's wife –which probably explains a lot about the Naval Cadets kit inspection. We managed to get back 'On Shore' with a full complement of men and some great memories of our Matelot friends –

Richard RE (almost RN)

ALEC LYNN
A New Beginning

Don't be down and don't be sad.
Like always, I'm not all bad.
I try my best to do things right.
My nightmares still get me in the night.
I'm wet with sweat when I awake
Wondering how much more I've got to take.
A new beginning I was told
But not when it would start to unfold.
Do I deserve it when others can't
Be here with us to smell the plants,
Or see the trees, the birds, the spring,
The wondrous things that they might bring.
A future of what, I ask myself.
Of fighting with my head,
Sweating in my bed?
I have more than most, a wife,
A house, a family, a cat.
Some of the lads don't have all that.
A new beginning – do I deserve it?
I'm hard on myself, that I do know.
I try very hard not to let it show.
I joke and laugh when I am here
To hide the pain that is always near.
This must be it. My new beginning.

CONNOR JEWEL

It's A Beautiful World

Our beautiful world
Has mountains with cloud-covered tips,
Rivers that flow and fish perform a show.
The sky which is as blue as water,
Water as pure as pure may be,
While the buildings that say *Look, we're amazing.*
Look at our world,
Our beautiful world,
Hills covered in green ferns,
Its own place in space,
Towering trees as big as a church.
Look at our world
Our beautiful world
People running around
Children playing without a sound.
Look at our world as good as gold.

MARTIN 'SPIKE' DUNKIN

2002 Pilgrimage

We've not forgotten
We are still here
Just come back down
To shed a tear
To let you know
Despite your pain
Your sacrifice
Was not in vain

ALAN WALKER

Surplus to Requirements

You've done your time and done your bit,
served your country through all of it.
You've sweated tears and sweated blood
through streets abroad and fields of mud.

It's time to leave and settle down
you've done your bit for Queen and Crown.
How proud you were with all your mates,
you smoked and drank and went on dates.

You got in fights both good and bad,
you've laughed and cried, been mad and sad.
That time has passed. It's been and gone,
it's Civvy Street for you my son.

You struggle through with work and home,
frustrated, angry to the bone.
The only things that keep you sane
are happy memories that remain.

Then nightmares start and madness stains
the only hope you still retain.
Inside your head, thoughts invade,
you sometimes wish that you were dead.

Nobody understands your moods –
maybe it's something on the news,
a little thing that someone says –
You'll knock them down, your knuckles red.

The Government says that they will help.
They've got the power, they've got the clout.
But faceless bureaucrats will shout,
They've done their time, they're all washed out.

You can rant and rage and shout out loud
and raise your voice above the crowd
No matter how much anger vents,
you're surplus to requirements.

Manoeuvre

Lying on a rain-
soaked patch
of land. This is it –
where we make our stand.

We know
we are surrounded
with no chance
of rescue.

This is what
it's all
come down to.
Stand to.

Stand to.
Alert.
Ready.
Eyes are watching,
nerves are steady.

A rustle of fallen leaves
and crack of twigs
reveals the location
of the others in this.

I wonder
what thoughts
are going through their minds –
is this my last push,
the end of the line?

Waving shivering branches.
A shape,
shadowed but moving.
A glint of metal says they are closing.

A gap of about 100 metres,
no, make that 90,
separates
the two warring parties.

ENDEX!
Exercise over.
Get in the wagons.
The hot showers are waiting.

Dream and Shadow

I live in a world
of dream and shadow
where only others of my kind
understand the torment.

Fearful that I might
expose that which
I have become,
far removed from reality.

I do not like to
be involved
with the business
of everyday

For me it
does not exist.
Something inside has
gone to sleep.

Silence, silence –
ssshh the thoughts
that tear through
and mix themselves …

Mix in and await
the ambush moment –
out of the shadows
and into the dream.

Iraq 2003

Shimmering heat haze,
waves in the desert sun
run waterlike
into loose and never-ending sand.

Days turn to night,
ground soaked in dew to frost
illuminated by a million stars
magnificent in the heavens.

Please God, please
not tonight.
If you are out there
hear what I say.

Huddled in sleeping bags
like maggots
writhing wriggling
each with their own thoughts.

What will tomorrow bring
in fierce burning sun,
done down and weary
boredom achieves so much that's dreary.

Move forward as a whole
a vast sandstorm
rolling toward
a waiting foe.

Gas Alert

The night is still and quiet
so quiet –
shattered by metal on metal,
vehicle horns, shouting

GAS, GAS, GAS.
Automatic reactions,
be in time mask in nine.
Nine seconds to stay alive.

After years of training
and practice
it all comes down to
this moment.

Hands down to the left,
respirator sack ripped open,
the feel of rubber and glass –
mask on, follow procedure,

a multitude of Gas Gas Gas
blow hard
check for fit,
check your mates for symptoms.

This is not a drill –
the adrenaline pumping
subsides to fear.
Christ this is for real.

In Remembrance

Remember
Remember those who went before
Remember those who gave their lives to war
Remember the ultimate sacrifice

Remember those that chose to give
that others continued to live
Remember the wounded and the maimed
Remember those that carry mental scars

Remember them
Remember them all
Remember the ones who continue to fall
No more tomorrows

Remember those who stood to be counted
to give up their comforts
stand against those
who would cause harm

Remember, mothers, fathers
Brothers, sons, daughter, sister
Remember the soldier
Who stands before all, tall and proud

PETER DOBSON

Autumn

The wood is changing
Life is rearranging
Leaves are glowing
Streams are flowing

Wind is blowing
Fruits are ripening
Rain is falling
Hunters go hunting

Animals are collecting
Food for eating
Birds are leaving
For warmth of wintering

The Truth

The truth is a word which is all things
to all men.

To politicians obfuscating is a way
of life.

The victor writes the truth as they
want to.

Certainly not as things really
happened.

Truth changes with each and
every telling.

Embellishments and changes abound.

Within a few repeats, there is nothing
of the original.

The media bend the truth to fit
their point of view.

They say pictures never lie.
Have you ever used an airbrush?

What is P.T.S.D.?

What is P.T.S.D.?
It is the night.
It is forever dark.
You feel the pain.
You are the guilt.
You weep, you scream.
It all comes back.
You hide, you cower.
You cover your eyes
Wherever you see the fright.
You're scared to sleep.
You're scared to wake.
You wake, you scream.
You sleep, you weep.

The Man Inside Little Mouse

When away from Tyrwhitt House
I show a different persona to the world.
I'm down and quiet with little humour
Because inside I'm a little mouse.

The man of fun and games that I used to be
Is buried so deeply, no-one knows it's there.
I'm sometimes terrified and lost,
There's no-one who understands.

Within the house things change
I'm more outgoing jokes and laughter
pervade the atmosphere mixing with
others is so easy they all know.

We laugh we joke we get release from
anger, frustration, feeling scared. We're
nervous coming we're nervous going
But still we come to get release.

Each visit makes us stronger the feelings
are hidden but still return
before we know it. Back to the
little scared mice we are outside.

No Fool Me

I joined the army
should have stayed at school
taken my GCEs
More fool me
Joined Junior Leaders R.A.
No fool me
Had to have a reset on the Plotter
in my survey exam
lost survey prize because of it
More fool me
Joined man service good Regt
No fool me
Asked to go to the Far East
Sent to Shoeburyness (can't get
Further east in England)
More fool me
Main trade signaller not surveyor
More fool me
Bollocked a Major on Regt. Net
Held up my promotion
More fool me
Got married in 79
No fool me
Made redundant in 84
More fool me
Played rugby for 35 years
No fool me
Taught kids rugby for 10 years
No fool me
Found Combat Stress
No fool me

Fantastic support here
No fool me
can't work now
More fool me
Volunteer to help council tenants
No fool me.

JOHN SIMON

I'm Sitting Making Poppies

I'm sitting making poppies.

I've never worn a poppy.

I'm sitting making poppies.

I used to run a mile,
I'd see them on the corner,
tin in hand,
part of that bloody band.

I'm sitting making poppies.

I'd hide,
do anything to avoid them,
head held low,
I'd walk quickly by.
No way would I wear a poppy –
it's only another bloody show.

I'm sitting making poppies.

I sat down here tonight,
all the stuff to make a poppy,
laid upon the table top.
Black buttons,
green stalks
and bloody red poppy tops.

I'm sitting making tear-stained poppies.
It now means such a lot.
The blood spilled all around me
from the mates who meant a lot.

I'll wear that bloody poppy.

It meant such a bloody lot.

GAVIN THOMSON

Hollybush

Heroes we help through day-time and night
To tell you you're not alone in this fight.
Let down your guard and trust us each day
Lower your arms and at peace you may lay.
Young ones and old together as one
Be not afraid you can shine like the sun.
Uniforms gone and you each gave your best
Soldiers no more for now you may rest
And honour we will, your every request.

ALAN BELL

Come Judgement Day

Hey big man, yeah – you upstairs,
what do you think of me?
As you'll be my judge some day,
will I ever be set free?

I know you know the sins I've sinned,
the wrongs that I have done.
My faith in you I once replaced
with women, wine and gun.

You made me in your image
like many many more
which makes you kind of sick in mind
and rotten to the core.

I won't be coming to your house
to beg on bended knee.
I need not your shoulder
or misguided sympathy.

So ask yourself a question God.
Take time and answer well.
If heaven's full of fucked up minds
then what's it like in Hell?

ERIC THORNTON

Off Switch

If god had invented an off switch, would I be able to get
  some sleep
Would I live a normal life, would I ever be called deep?

If god had invented an off switch, could I imagine my
  day to day,
Could I manage a good relationship, could I bring home
  better pay?

If god had invented an off switch, should you want to stay
  with me,
Should you always hold my hand, should you never
    have to plea?

If god had invented an off switch, will we listen to our heart
Will we always want to cuddle, will we just simply part?

Sounding Board

Our first meeting was full of fear.
What would she think?
What would she hear?
I tried so hard to be real strong,
Would she have a magic wand?

I was shy hurt and weak
Crying out loud I feel a freak.
Would she think I was pathetic?
She was totally empathetic.

She helped me to carry on,
To stand up and tell and be strong.
She helped me through my troubled days,
With hope and help and listening ears.

Being believed is the best thing ever,
Soon maybe I'll no longer feel a sinner.
Now my life might move on,
I'll do her proud and carry on.

MAXINE GENTLE

Depression, Tears, Anger

I have been to the darkest place in the world,
But I did not move.

I have fought against the worst demons,
But I did not fight.

I held back a great river,
But I did not get wet.

I put out a ball of fire,
But I did not get burnt.

I did this all at the same time,
In this little place of mine –

The safest place I could be,
Inside of me.

Soldier, Soldier

Soldier soldier
where have you gone?
Soldier soldier
I am here all alone
Soldier soldier
It's very dark
Soldier soldier
have a pain in my heart
Soldier soldier
come set me free
Soldier soldier
it cannot be
Soldier soldier
tell me it's not true
Soldier soldier
I wish I could hold you
Soldier soldier
here I am without you
loving you
missing you

BLACKDOG661

Mental Torment

There is an itch
constantly there,
it makes me twitch
I am in fear
of the thoughts
they drive me spare
'cos it is deep inside
in the only place
that I cannot scratch –
my mind

The Great Leveller

How tall are you?
the Sergeant asked.
Six Foot one I replied
Bollocks he retorted.
To the next in line,
the same question,
the reply to which
he only snorted.
To all in line,
the question asked
the replies to which,
he said were *Arse.*
You are only as tall
the Khaki god intoned
As your rifle
        Forty-three inches[1]
As I was to learn
a rifle is called a weapon,
so pity today's soldier,
when the Battlefield on
whose weapon is a mere
thirty-one inches[2]
all told
and the poor Civvy[3],
who, despite making bold,
on his 'weapon'
has no inches at all!

---

1   43 inches – the length of the SLR (Self Loading Rifle) the standard British Army
    rifle at the time (1980).
2   31 inches – the length of the SA80 Assault Rifle (more correctly the Rifle 5.56
    the current standard British Army Rifle.
3   Civvy – Civilian.

Tuesday 9ᵗʰ September 1980, 10:30pm

What is a fuck pig?
It can't be very nice,
I know what a tube is,
'cos I am one, apparently,
incapable of sorting out my locker,
or making a bed pack,
or pressing my P.T. kit
we're not good enough
to wear a uniform yet,
it would offend the real soldiers.

Change parades,
two minutes to run up three flights of stairs,
change into whatever uniform they say,
then back on parade –
totally impossible
with the time they give.

Standing up when a superior
(that's everyone else, except you,
in case you didn't know)
enters the room, all present leaping up,
like startled cows about to stampede,
at the command
STAND UP.

Being taught how to press your kit,
personal hygiene an alien subject
to some of the boys.
Lots of shouting and screaming,
Paddy Black, our Sergeant,

a professional soldier
expressing his dismay.

Even with everything that I
have learnt or
not learned properly,
it seems since 12:00 today
sabotaging his best efforts apparently,
I try to please this screaming god
But still I am no good.

What is a fuck pig?

Sarin

Sarin is a nerve agent
an incapacitant to be exact
(Don't I know)
The second to be discovered
by a Doctor Schrader, Gerhardt,
hence it is known as
G.B. for German B
(Don't I know.)
German A is Tabun
(now this I don't know)
And Soman or German D
(now this I don't know)
No one knows why,
there is no German C
But
Sarin is a Nerve Agent,
In the class of incapacitants.
(Don't I know...)

Sarin 2

Ta
Bu
n-
GA
Sarin-GB Nerve
S
O
M
A
N
—
G
D

Thank god they were never used properly
(But don't forget the Kurds and the Tokyo attacks)

Sarin 3 (1983)

I stood erect, and straight of back
My legs were straight
(and in those days my chest was sound).
No way back –
I turned towards the fluorescent light of white,
Nowhere was shadow black.

I marched towards my destiny,
wide awake I strode, my boots brush-polished.
Rested, booted and puttied, at that moment not in a tizzy.

Feeling on top of the world, it was a lark.
No hostile action or enemy to blame, even so –
my 'friend' the scientist, safely behind.
No respirator for me, just the gas-tight door
and beyond, my destiny.
The technician already in his S6 respirator.

No yelling or screaming, only the metronome's relentless
ticking.
No pain for me – that would follow – I felt – something
for contributing to science and defence.
Looking up and seeing the scientists behind a clear
window which for them was air tight,
my chest was tightening to coincide
with the relentless metronome's ticking.
The hardness of breath would come to me
far sooner than I had expected.

I start to choke but carry on, only the technician observing.
You cannot dream of my feeling or the start of the suffering.
Meiosis setting in,
the scientists observing, safe in their citadel.
Where they watch, the metronome dictating my pace –
that bloody metronome.

The lie they had told me, their wicked sin.
If you could have heard my laboured wheezing,
my lungs not yet fully corrupted,
you cannot feel the pain I was feeling setting in.

My pupil's constricting, breathing harder,
the trace of Sarin to be recorded in my blood –
so many needles to come.
The pain of photographing my retinas, still constricting,
of blood samples taken, electrical probes into nerves in my
arms.
The lie that this test was necessary and harmless.
Three deaths and matchless suffering
ignored as an inconvenient story.
So many of us, it became
our collective story.

WAYNE FRANCIS

The Tree

We haven't got all day my lad,
the sergeant said to me.
You need to use your discipline,
on this side of the tree.
Get hold of your trenching tool,
we don't have time on our side.
Remember the other battles,
when we would dig and hide.
Make sure the hole is as big as you,
they will need all our protection.
Don't forget wild animals,
These lads don't want detection.
Do your best to get ten dug,
don't curse, lest you be heard.
I want the rifle put in that way,
to attract the smallest bird.
Check that they are spaced evenly,
uniform's the word we seek.
Come on now bite your lip,
don't stand there feeling meek.

That was thirty years ago
the sergeant was ahead of me.
Buried alongside all the rest,
on this side of the tree.

GRAHAM CULTON
See Me for Who I Am

Please don't look at me differently,
I only accept support and empathy.

Many a place I have been,
and too many horrors I have seen

On many roads, at many junctions –
never understanding psychological function.

For 'Queen and Country' I was loyal
though my head filled with traumatic turmoil.

I find it hard to leave my troubles behind.
All this leaves me a shattered mind.

I share my pain with my brothers and sisters in arms.
We all have individual distinctive alarms.

My colours – they were green and brown
from the day I gave my oath of allegiance to the Crown.

Notes on the Contributors

JAY ASHWORTH

I lost my mind and found it again at Combat Stress. I own the tools to live and strive for better, thanks to Combat Stress. I understand compassion towards myself, through guidance from Barbara at Combat Stress – art, words, expression and honest emotions give me strength to focus.

ANGUS BINNIE

I am a retired Probation Officer in my eighties. I spent nearly five months in the front line before being wounded in both legs on 9th March, 1945. Since retiring I have been involved with the local art group as a watercolour artist, and for the past fifteen years I have been a member of Tyne and Esk Writers with some success in poetry and short story writing. Combat Stress lectures in Edinburgh have regularly attracted my attendance.

RICHARD BORYER

I was born on 20 December 1962, in Portsmouth. I was a member of RAMC TA and served in the 1st Gulf War. I am unable to speak and use a Lightwriter to 'talk'; this was bought by the Royal British Legion.

KEITH BURTON

Keith now lives in Chatham and is engaged to Dorothy. His daughter Leah, her partner Dan, grandson Kieran and stepson Ashley live in Maidstone.

Amidst life's journey obstacles arise hindering progress
A titanic struggle ensues to discover safe passage
Through the mind's dark regions
Mapping the route with poetry.

GRAHAM CULTON

I served in the Queen's Own Highlanders (Highlanders) from 1993–2003, when I was medically discharged. Served with the U.N. in Bosnia from 1994 till 1995. Several Tours in Northern

Ireland. Six months as a Patrol Dog Handler, and two years as a Naval Vehicle Search Dog Handler in N.I. Joined the Army for travel and adventure, and to do something positive in life. I have a seven-year-old daughter who is the light of my life. Most recently, I've worked as a Fire Marshall at the Paralympics, having completed time working at the Olympics.

PETER 'THE HAT' DOBSON

I am a 64-year-old ex-artilleryman. At fifteen I went into boys' service in the Junior Leaders Regt., RA. After two years I left and went to various units over the next twenty years as radio operator/ surveyor/ driver and I enjoyed these very much before I was made redundant. I did various jobs in Civvy Street, then in the mid-nineties my flashbacks and nightmares became worse. I was diagnosed with PTSD in 1999 at Combat Stress. In 2007 I was introduced to poetry and art, and realised that I enjoyed them. Then in 2009 I conceived the idea for a poetry volume in support of Combat Stress, so now after three years you can peruse the fruits of our labour.

JANET DOWNS

I'm a retired secondary school teacher and grandparent. My parents were both in the RAF in WW2 and met in Ceylon (now Sri Lanka). I go to Creative Writing classes at Peterborough City College with author Tim Wilson (aka Jude Morgan and Hannah March) who inspired me to write the poem. Although retired, I am now an educational researcher and blog on the Local Schools Network.

MARTIN 'SPIKE' DUNKIN

I was just 20 when I went to war with the Royal Navy in the Falklands in 1982. The sights and sounds that I saw changed my life and I was diagnosed with PTSD in 2002 following a pilgrimage to the islands. I wrote this poem to attach to the three wreaths that I laid to remember my fellow servicemen who made the ultimate sacrifice. I now attend Combat Stress on a regular basis and find that art and writing help me cope with my problems. I'm just a normal bloke with a few problems.

IAN FOULKES (BLACKDOG661)

In 1980 Ian joined the Royal Corps of Signals and was trained at the Army Apprentices College, Harrogate. He graduated in 1982. In 1983 he was exposed to Sarin Nerve Agent at Porton Down. He served mainly overseas; Germany, Northern Ireland and Norway being just some of his postings. Ian was awarded a Commander-in-Chief's commendation. He had many interesting and diverse roles, both with Royal Signals and while detached. Ian left the Army in 1999 as a Sergeant.

LINDA FOULKES

Linda works full time for a local authority as well as caring for her husband, who suffers with late onset PTSD. She has spoken on national radio about the effects of living with PTSD and tries to be as open as possible with others to aid understanding of the condition. The poem, 'Night', was written in her head on the drive home from work after a particularly unsettled night's sleep.

WAYNE FRANCIS

I was born the son of a Royal Navy sailor and my great uncle was the most decorated serviceman of the First World War, a sailor to boot. I joined because job prospects were not good for me where I grew up, but I loved the life immediately.

The Falklands War couldn't have happened at a worse time for me – straight out of training and in my mind totally out of my depth. This continued to haunt me, so I self-medicated and alcoholism followed. When I left the Navy I went from job to job and by the time I was thirty-five I was a drink-dependent alcoholic. I should have called out for help, with my Falklands demons and also the aftermath of the first Gulf War, but I drank to block it all out.

Thankfully Combat Stress came to the rescue and now I work as an educational worker. I have been to university and have not had a drink for five years. I hope to have my own house later this year. People often ask me would I do the Falklands again and I reply I would do it ten times again because I am a firm believer in determination and, at long last, I realise that I am lucky to be here. I still suffer in my mind, but I'm making changes to bring about my wellbeing by accepting the help on offer and not dwelling too much on the past.

For me, this poem raises ideas on the futility of war, the sense of duty many of us accept and a respect that can never be paid back fully.

MAXINE GENTLE

My name is Maxine Gentle and I am 22 years old. I lost my brother when he was killed in action in Iraq in 2004. I was 14. Losing a sibling is the hardest thing I have ever had to deal with in my life. I wrote this poem to try to communicate how I was feeling and how you can look okay on the outside but be hurting on the inside. Writing has helped me to cope with my loss.

RICHARD GILDEA

A retired War Pensioner having served in the Armed Forces as a member of the Royal Engineers. A career as a Drilling Engineer/ Project Engineer followed, which involved substantial overseas travel. I am a father of three and grandfather of four. I enjoy writing poetry and creating works of art, activities which have helped as coping strategies in relation to ongoing medical problems.

LEE HARRISON

I was born in London in 1953 and after a happy childhood and school life I joined the Army. During my service I was posted to Northern Ireland. I left in 1976 but since then I have had years of torment and heartache. In 2012 I was given the chance to come to terms with my past. I am now finally at peace with myself and enjoying life.

LAURENCE HEWINGS

When I left the Royal Marines I trained as a manager with a leading brewery and ran mainly 'difficult' pubs for over ten years in and around London. Then, regretfully, I took a wrong turn and ended up as a member of a national outlaw biker gang where after fourteen years, the realization that I would end up either in prison or dead prompted me to leave and start a new life. Now at fifty years old, I live quietly in the Devon countryside with my wife and two young boys; with a third boy due very soon. In my spare time I love writing and cartooning, and I also work voluntarily with young offenders.

RAY HEWITT
I was deployed on Operation Granby aged nineteen and my experiences led to a diagnosis of PTSD several years later. I spent time at Tyrwhitt House and received massive help from Combat Stress. I now work as a Wiring Engineer and have blogged about my experiences at http://bloodinthesand.blogspot.com/. I have also written a book which is currently being edited by my agent.

SHAUN JOHNSON
Shaun Johnson served in the British Army for nearly twelve years until a crush injury forced him to take early retirement from service. Over the years Shaun battled and hid an invisible condition, PTSD, from his friends and family before coming forward to finally have treatment at Combat Stress in 2009. Today Shaun is a Shakespearean actor with the newly formed Combat Veteran Players theatre company whose cast is made up of veterans suffering similar conditions. Writing the poem 'Summertime Days' helped me to look to the light instead of the darkness every time I read it back. It kind of makes me smile and takes me to a place of tranquillity and safety.

CONNOR JEWELL
Aged 11 years. I live in Somerset with my Mum, Pa and our two horses. I do karate, Sea Cadets and Pony Club as I love horse riding. I have my own horse and often ride out with my Pa when he rides his horse which I love as it's our time together – Son and Pa time, I call it. I also love reading and writing. I wrote the poem 'It's a Beautiful World' for Pa to take with him on one of his visits to Tyrwhitt House.

RICHARD KIDGELL

Richard Kidgell was an electronics technician in the Royal Air Force from 1978–1985. His service included working on and close to the targets of an air-to-ground weapons range for over three years, including several months under IRA terrorist threat. Following service he worked for over 21 years as a systems design engineer for GEC-Marconi Radar and Defence Systems Ltd., before taking medical early retirement in 2006 because of increasingly severe symptoms of Post Traumatic Stress Disorder. Richard has been receiving treatment for PTSD from Combat Stress since 2004.

PAUL LOMAX

Thirty-seven years old. Diagnosed with PTSD after returning from Iraq in 2005. Combat Stress has been my lifeline. My poem 'Why' sums up my life since Iraq. I still am in the desert.

ALEC LYNN

Former Royal Marine Sergeant 1961–1977. Commando through and through. I signed on for twenty-two years but my career was cut short due to injuries received whilst serving with 45 Commando.

Thirty-seven years after my traumas I went for a walkabout for five months. Needed time out, I was later told. On my return I was hit by a bolt from hell called Combat PTSD. I would not wish this on my worst enemy.

Seven years later I am still waiting for my new beginning. Things got even worse though I thought they couldn't. Combat Stress is fighting my battles with me. Thank God for them! Tomorrow is a new day. Let's start again.

STUART MCGLEAVE

I was born in Dunfermline in 1972, raised in Bathgate, and now live in Ayrshire. I left School with three O-Levels in English, French and Craft & Design, and gained employment as an apprentice plumber. But I was made redundant in 1992.

I then applied to join the Army where I became a member of the Pipes and Drums and played in the Edinburgh Military Tattoo. I did four tours of Northern Ireland. When I left the Army in 2000 I worked at Stansted and Edinburgh Airports. I also worked for Royal Mail for five years. However I had turned to alcohol and heavy gambling. I lost contact with my family and was homeless for about eight months.

I then managed to get a meeting with a Combat Stress Welfare Officer. I was diagnosed with PTSD in 2008. I am now alcohol free and I don't gamble anymore, thanks to AA and GA meetings and continued support from all at Hollybush House. I am now on a treatment programme with medication for my PTSD. Also, through the help of Welfare at Hollybush, I am in regular contact with my daughter Jasmine, who now lives in New Zealand with her mother. I started writing poetry because I find it therapeutic and it helps my mental state.

JOEY JOE MCGUIRE

A native of Newcastle, he was brought up in post-war poverty. His education was interrupted when he emigrated to the USA but as the war raged in Vietnam he was sent home to avoid the draft – only to join the Parachute Regiment and serve two tours of Northern Ireland: The Ardoyne and South Armagh. He has been able to overcome his many Everests by turning to his only true love, poetry. The life, books, poetry and music of Chelsea poet, Joey Joe McGuire in association with the Sir Oswald Stoll home for disabled servicemen.

CHRIS MOORE

In 1979 I left school with no formal qualifications, joined the Merchant Navy Training College and received three months of training before joining my first ship, R.F.A. *Appleleaf.* We sailed from our home port of Portland, Dorset on January 2nd 1980 and two months later arrived in the Persian Gulf where we received war bonus pay as the Gulf had been declared a war zone as part of the Iran–Iraq war. I was sixteen. At seventeen, on board the super tanker, *Limatula*, I sailed back to the Persian Gulf. It was still a war zone.

At eighteen I joined R.F.A. *Tidespring* and sailed from Gibraltar to the South Atlantic. The first M.O.D to enter the Falklands war zone, and I was present at South Georgia on the night Argentina surrendered. On my nineteenth birthday *Tidespring* received 185 Argentinian POWs, and our crew enjoyed excellent relations with them. *Tidespring* went on to play a significant role in the recapture of South Georgia and the Falkland Islands.

In August 1982 I arrived back in Portsmouth to a huge reception. The South Atlantic Central Campaign medal arrived via the post-lady six weeks later.

LIAM O'BRIEN

Born in a small town in West Yorkshire. Went on to serve ten years in the RAF as part of the catering unit, 1997–2007 TG19. Currently suffers from PTSD and with the help of Combat Stress hoping to overcome my illness and have a fairly normal life.

EDWARD (TED) OGLE

I joined the Army as a boy soldier in 1962, training to be an Armourer. I passed out in 1965, coming top in military training and second in trade training, my final report describing me as a "dedicated soldier". Twelve years later as a Staff Sergeant Artificer Weapons I was medically discharged from RVH *Netley*. My admission was the result of a suicide attempt following my last tour of duty in N.I. In about 1994 I came down to Tyrwhitt House where I was diagnosed with PTSD, due to the various active service postings I had undergone. This was the start of coming to terms with my illness and the development of my coping mechanisms – an ongoing process which continues to the present day.

DAVE PAYNE

I have spent most of my life on the water: as a child racing sailing dinghies, canoeing, rowing, sailing on square-rigged tall ships and working on my father's trawler during school holidays and weekends. I served on minesweepers in the Royal Navy and had the misfortune to be involved in minesweeping operations in the Gulf during 1987–1988. On leaving the RN I held a variety of jobs, a gypsum miner being one of them, but could never settle in them, which led me back to sea working on trawlers. Now I'm a full-time carer for my disabled partner, and a patient of Combat Stress.

RICHARD PEACOCKE

I am an ex-soldier who once disposed of bombs, and an ex-prison officer nurse. I have been mentally unwell for many years and in that time, during the darkest days, I have found that reading and writing poetry has been very therapeutic. I suppose the major driver behind my writing is that it allows me to reflect on my distress in a condensed and clear way. That it is also meaningful to other readers, and in that I might offer them a little of the solace I find for myself behind the words, is a great benefit.

PAUL PERCIVAL

I spent fifteen years in the Royal Marines and served in Northern Ireland, with the UN, Cyprus and the Falklands War. Before being diagnosed I had been living rough on the streets for three-and-a-half years, three years in alcohol rehabilitation units and seven years in detoxes. I knew I was ill. But when diagnosed three years ago I cried like a baby to know I wasn't the only one. Severe Post Traumatic Stress Disorder. Depression. Thank God for Combat Stress, but shame on the MoD. The doc said that I have had PTSD since 1976 after a terrible mortar attack in Crossmaglen. I just cracked on as you do – don't want to be seen as a failure even though it's not your fault that you are ill.

PETER PUGH

Born of a RAF family. Evacuated from the 1958 Baghdad Revolution as a child. As a teenager I watched the RAF Thor nuclear missiles, sweating in anticipation during the terrifying days of the Cuba crisis. A veteran logistician of the Cold War who endeavoured to ensure our ability to strike back. Now thankful for the care of Combat Stress following a tragic loss.

CHARLIE RIDLEY (THE RIDDLER)

Born in Leamington Spa in 1958 I grew up in care, joining the Royal Marines as a Junior Marine and advised I could be a chef. After training, and before reaching 18, I took the free discharge and rejoined the Army to be a chef, only to be hijacked at the recruit selection centre and trained instead as a tank driver then sent at just 18 on emergency posting to Northern Ireland as an infantry foot soldier/radio operator to a unit not in my own regiment. As with many other 'boys', for that was what we were, frontline service had a profound effect on me, both from what I witnessed and was ordered to do with no psychological or physical preparation or training. For me, writing poetry was the only way I could return from patrol, and find any solace, reason, or peace from the horrors and turmoil within. Later, detached, moving to the border, patrol on foot, land rover, and OPs, the events that followed took away my life as I knew it, and my innocence forever. After two years in hospital, I was medically discharged back into civvy life alone. 'Exemplary Military Conduct' having no bearing on my civilian future or medical support, the road ahead was what I made of my life. Many, many times over the years, still haunted by those dark days, the smells, taste of fear, sights and sounds that never leave me still, all those who served will know reading this, the poetry I wrote then, gives some semblance, some reason, if not answers, to why and at times a reason for still empty tears. Two years ago, after all those years of being I thought 'On my own' with my service and injuries, it was only when I attended the service of thanksgiving 'Operation Banner' at St Paul's Cathedral was I both profoundly shocked and saddened to see, the so many others like me. For the first time in 36 years, apart from my poetry, I had found some unspoken understanding, comfort, bond with others like me who knew and know, endured, and still do, the horrors of war. If my poems, through their innocence and naive humour, give some comfort and understanding to others that they are not alone then, after all these years, there has been reason for the words I wrote at a time that gave me some comfort, took away my 'innocence' and changed my life and spirit forever. Thank you for reading them.

JAMIE ROWLAND – Cover Photographer
I served as an Infantry Soldier with 1st Battalion the 22nd (Cheshire) Regiment (now 1 Mercian) for ten years until 2004 after completing 7 operational tours. Two years ago, I was diagnosed with PTSD, after suffering a complete meltdown, which cost me my business and very nearly my marriage, family and life. Where many veterans turn to alcohol and drugs as a form of self-medicating, I became a workaholic. It goes without saying that losing my business after my breakdown left a massive hole in my life, which is when my lead worker at Audley Court (PTSD Treatment Centre) suggested I learn a new hobby to occupy my mind. I developed an interest in photography and, since then, I have managed to self teach this wonderful art … though I still have so much to learn!! That said, I can honestly say photography (along with my pet Rottweiler – Bruce) has literally been a life saver for me. In fact, I have recently decided to take the plunge and go professional and see what happens!
I have recently returned home after my 3rd visit to Audley Court and whilst I still have a long way to go in my recovery, I am continuing to learn to live with the condition through alternative therapies. During my last stay I happened to be out in the gardens taking pictures of wildlife when I noticed this rainbow. I feel the light and warmth of the image signifies so much about the peace and tranquillity of the gardens at Audley Court. However, more importantly, I also want the image to send a message to other Combat Stress sufferers that there is a pot of gold at the end of the rainbow … it is called life!

GAVIN THOMSON
I spent nearly four years in the Army. I now spend my time writing with hope that I can help whoever reads my work. I know I have had success in that department for which I am grateful.

ERIC THORNTON
I am 43 years old and I have been regularly going to Hollybush House for just over a year now, though I did go over 10 years ago but at the time I was not ready for help. I joined the Army in 1985 and left in 1992. I was in the Argyll and Sutherland Highlanders

and I served in three operational tours of Northern Ireland. I have been diagnosed with PTSD and clinical depression. In the past I have been in very dark places (mentally) which is where the inspiration for most of my writing comes from. I also have severe dyslexia, so spellcheck is always a must for me. I am married with one child and life is always one step forward three steps backwards – but hey, at least I'm moving.

ALAN WALKER

I spent time serving with both Regular and Reserve Forces on operations in Bosnia (5), Kosovo (2) and the Iraq War in 2003. I was diagnosed with PTSD in 2007. Creative writing has been something of a find for me, along with photography – both of which were introduced by Combat Stress. It has been an enormous surprise to be selected for the anthology. I am extremely proud to have been selected. Heartfelt thanks must go to everyone who has helped me on this journey.

MARK WALMSLEY

Mark Walmsley is a 58-year-old, resides in Torpoint, S.E. Cornwall and is a former Royal Navy Submariner having served nineteen-and-a-half years between 1976–1995. He was invalided out with mental and physical disabilities. Subsequently, Mark obtained an Honours degree with a view to teaching. Sadly, the depth of his infirmities has taken a number of years to ascertain. 2007 was his salvation: his left knee was replaced and so was hope – in the form of diagnosis, treatment, therapy and support to deal with PTSD at Combat Stress. He is enjoying projects in the field of art and literature which give him optimism for the future. He owes a debt of gratitude to his friends, Church Legion, Local Housing/Mental Health Teams, The Veterans Agency, so many people.

JIM WELSHMAN

My name is Jim Welshman. I am 59 years old. I live in Norfolk a few miles from the coast at Great Yarmouth. I served in 2nd Battalion Royal Green Jackets (during the height of The Troubles). I've worked mainly in the security industry since leaving H.M. Forces. I was diagnosed with chronic PTSD in 2010, and with the help of Combat Stress I'm trying to rebuild my life one day at a time. I thank all at Tyrwhitt House for giving me the opportunity of a better future.

GRAHAM WOODHALL

I was born in a very dingy hospital in Bond Street, Leicester in 1947 – baby boomer time. My first five years were spent in a Nissen hut and a condemned dwelling in the slums. Then we had a council house. Due to the influence of my Grandma's and the Boys' Brigade, all I wanted to do was join the Royal Navy. In 1962 I did just that at the famous HMS *Ganges* in Suffolk. Twenty-eight years later, metaphorically battered and bruised I started a normal life; outside.

I struggled at work for a few years until my GP said that's enough. My confused mind has kept me busy since and now I'm nearly sane. I enjoy railway modelling, gardening, my car and my family but I hate what is happening to my country. I am now an OAP and ready for future adventures, which I look forward to with optimism. If I could, I would run the country and let the world leave us behind, so that as an island we could drift back into our glorious past and live the life my forefathers used to live – happy with no knowledge of the outside world.

[Note: Some authors appear more than once within the text as thematic threads of courage and strength are being explored.]